EX LIBRIS

"The ludicrous, the grotesque, and the abject, are striking elements in the pen of Dr. Will Liangco, whose 49 'tales' in this debut collection treat the gore of the medical profession with the comic relief of caricature. The gift of dark humor is a difficult thing to handle, and only a few Filipino writers wield it with panache. But in his hands, this penchant for exaggerating the taboo and giving one final ironic twist to the knife, do not fail to provoke uneasy laughter, leading to a more serious attention on the structural poverty that afflicts many Filipinos seeking public health service. Exposed through Dr. Will's critical eye, we see in his creative nonfiction narratives his duress as a medical student, a resident, a fellow, and a consultant, as he cares for patients who also have to go through the interminable hurdles and hoops of applying for government subsidy for medical treatment and care.

That he chose oncology for his specialization places him in daily proximity with serious illness and death. He says in *Alleviations*, that he chose to train in oncology to access facilities, experts, and clinical trials that would alleviate his father's struggle with primary liver cancer. But we discover in the story the real reason: Dr. Will's kindness to his patients comes from his father's advise as a cancer patient and a dying parent: 'Never be late for your clinic...don't be one of those doctors who make patients wait for hours, only to shoo them out of the room after a rushed consult. Always be nice to them, especially the elderly. Never turn down people asking for help, even if the only motivation is to avoid potential guilt when they die.'

Dr. Will's heart and mind are in their right places, and we cheer him on, the way his mother does in *Private Practice Marketing Primer*, proudly giving strangers her doctor-son's calling cards and saying: '*Anak ko yan.*' "

— **Marjorie Evasco, PhD Litt. author of *Dreamweavers***

"For those of us on the receiving end of medicine, medical encounters can be daunting and depressing or hopeful and uplifting. A lot depends on the doctors, nurses, and other persons we entrust with our maladies. It is this social commentary behind the caricatures that resonated with me most deeply."

— **Catherine Rose Torres, author of *Sula's Voyage***

"These stories are deceptively breezy and funny. But one reads between the lines and realizes that here is a doctor who cares deeply for his patients, for others, and for the world. We are brought first-hand into the call rooms, the ER, faced with the drama and sanctity of patient care, realizing how difficult it is to go through medical school, residency, and fellowship training. Readers will enjoy the out-of-this-world experiences, starting with his supposed possession by an evil spirit as a child, or even during the time he had to search his heart and mind for the Tagalog word for 'cremation.' We learn new words like 'nanetting,' 'judgmental prognostication,' and 'hypochondriation.' Behind the laughter the pieces evoke, we see clearly the travails of the persona in the many different phases of his life, and we cheer him on, because we want him to succeed. This is the 'Other Side' of a doctor's life, and we commiserate with him in his human-ness, his foibles and misadventures, all told in a voice that is so self-deprecating one couldn't help but empathize and be one with him. This book is a tour de force, and a must-read!"

- **Alice M. Sun-Cua, MD, author of *Golden Kumquats in Trieste and Other Travel Tales***

"Will's '*Even Ducks Get Liver Cancer*' will move you to hysterical fits—and to tears. It lets you in on what you won't see in *Grey's Anatomy*, *Hospital Playlist*, and other Hollywood medical series— that med life isn't all like it's cracked up and glamourized to be, but, as with all that life throws us, it's better to go through it with friends, family, and humor."

- **Geraldine Zamora, MD, The Outstanding Women in the Nation's Service, awardee for Medicine, 2019**

"On the surface, the medical anecdotes in this collection seemingly intend to elicit laughter with their neologisms and characters with thinly-veiled alter-egos. Reading these tales closely, however, will reveal layers and layers of the author's authentic character: his deep compassion, effortless wit, daunting sharpness, and undeniable kindness. This book allows non-medical readers a rare glimpse of a doctor's life, reminiscent of A.B. Rotor's *The Men Who Play God* but suffused with unapologetic honesty in the middle of stark reality. For doctors, this book offers more than nostalgia and sentimentality. It encourages them to laugh their alveoli out and to weep with their soul."

- **Elvie Victonette Razon-Gonzalez, MD, author of *Vignettes of Voyages***

Dear Gail,

Hope um have fun reading...

EVEN
DUCKS
GET
LIVER
CANCER

and other medical misadventures

take care always,

WILFREDO LIANGCO

will liangco
Sept. 2022

MILFLORES
PUBLISHING, INC.

Even Ducks Get Liver Cancer and Other Medical Misadventures
Wilfredo Liangco

Published and exclusively distributed by

Milflores Publishing, Inc.
1244 E. Amang Rodriguez Avenue
De La Paz, Pasig City 1600
Philippines
info@milflorespublishing.com
www.milflorespublishing.com

MILFLORES
PUBLISHING, INC.

National Library of the Philippines CIP Data
Recommended entry:

Liangco, Wilfredo.
Even ducks get liver cancer : and other medical misadventures /
Wilfredo Liangco. — Pasig City : Milflores Publishing Inc.,
[2022], ©2022.
Pages ; cm

ISBN 978-971-828-121-5 (pb/bp)

1. Creative non-fiction, Philippine (English). 2. Life change
events in literature. 3. Physician's writings. I. Title.

808.887   PR9550.9.M37   2022   P220220106

Cover and book design by Mikke Gallardo

Printed in the Philippines

TABLE OF CONTENTS

THE BUTTERFLIES WE SHOULD HAVE MURDERED

TIME TO WORK

This book is dedicated
to my mother, Elena,
and to the loving memory
of my father, Eddie

INTRODUCTION

It's just as well that more physicians are not moonlighting as writers, because they have an unfair advantage over the common scribbler. The subject of literature is the human condition, and doctors are up to their elbows in it. The essential fact of the human condition is that we are all going to die: we are terrified by an inevitability that to doctors is not exactly an occupational hazard but an everyday worst-case scenario. This knowledge of our fragility and our stubborn capacity to endure is the stuff of literature, and that is where doctors set up camp. Hence Anton Chekhov, who basically invented the short story as we know it. Hence Arthur Conan Doyle, who created Sherlock Holmes. And Oliver Sacks, whose neurological case studies are moving testaments to the human spirit. And Jose Rizal, who only imagined this nation we belong to.

I doubt that Willy Liangco was pondering these things when he wrote this book, for they are the considerations that lead to performance anxiety in writers of any age. The first thing one notices upon reading him is the sheer pleasure he derives from putting words on paper. He is a lifelong reader—whenever anything happens he seems to be reading something. The second becomes apparent when food starts shooting out of the reader's nose: he's funny. He doesn't try to be funny (because that's the secret of not being funny), he simply views circumstances through a highly-developed sense of the ridiculous.

The third thing we notice is that in situations that would usually elicit fear, rage, anxiety, or grief, he sees humor. He is literally laughing in the face of death. It is often said that Filipinos crack jokes about the most serious subjects because we don't take anything seriously. (We certainly elect a lot of political jokes into office.) This may be so, but I also suspect that the Pinoy laugh reflex is a way of asserting a smidgin of power over a state of affairs we have no control over. It's the power of the powerless. You may be high and mighty, but we know what you really are. In Willy's writing, the all-powerful butt of the joke is mortality itself.

And when we finish laughing at the evil chicken, the fate of the medical students who graduate at the bottom of the class (it involves wire hangers), Nanette-ing With Conviction, the way to deliver a fatal diagnosis, whining competitions at The Shrine Motherfucker, Willy's reenactment of the escape through the sewers in The Shawshank Redemption, and the half-blessing, half-curse of being a doctor and a raging hypochondriac, we are struck by the common factor in these stories: Willy's unstinting humanity.

In "Into The Knacker" he recounts how, in the middle of a post-Typhoon Ondoy leptospirosis outbreak, a prisoner from the city jail is taken to the hospital by two policemen. He is in jail for double incest-rape. The prisoner soon falls into a coma and, after much begging and wheedling from Dr. Willy, a bed is found for him. The prisoner's wife arrives. She forgives him and asks that he be allowed to die at home. Between the mysterious new color-coding system for the patients ("I think yellow means very severe leptospirosis because it's the color of jaundice. Or is it...mild leptospirosis, because very severe things are supposed to be red?") and the policemen who will not let the comatose man out of their sight because he might escape, we get a picture of the harsh realities of the health care and criminal justice systems. A looming debate between retribution and forgiveness is resolved with the bleakest humor. We are all just people trying to eke out some life till we shuffle off this mortal coil.

In "Alleviations" we discover that Willy's decision to go into oncology sprang from a sense of duty towards his beloved father, a man with the compulsion to fix everything, who rigged up an emergency fire escape with a piece of cardboard attached saying, "Have No Fear!" It is a moving story poised between laughter and tears, the kind that makes doctors and writers.

When I met Willy in 2015 he had been writing to entertain himself and to stay sane in stressful times. He had refrained from discussing his life as a doctor because he thought it might be self-indulgent. Are you kidding, I said, and recited the first paragraph of this foreword, though not in the same words. Here, then, is the first of what should be many books from a doctor who writes, a writer who doctors, a person who understands that life is painful but we can't bear to leave it.

Jessica Zafra
Author, *The Age of Umbrage*

PREFACE

When I started an online journal back in 2006 I tried to avoid writing about the medical profession. I was concerned that the journal would sound too serious if I wrote about patient care, or too self-indulgent if I discussed the toils of medical training. There was also the conceit that there was more to me than this job. Keeping this resolve became a challenge when I went into internal medicine residency and medical oncology fellowship training. My life as a trainee was spent mostly inside the hospital, so what else was there to write about.

Thankfully, as I soon found out, not all stories in the hospital have to be about great tragedies or the triumphs of the human spirit. Sometimes there are stories about ordinary things, like disgruntled residents lounging around in a coffee shop, ranting, and gossiping about their terrible bosses. Not everyone gets to stab someone in the chest to release a pneumothorax, or deliver preterm twins in a restaurant, but many of the fellows have experienced hoarding leftovers from office lunches or whining about their much-delayed stipends. This compilation is mostly about those kinds of stories, dating from the time I was in training and up to the early years of private practice.

There were, of course, many harrowing moments that also needed to be told. Writing them has caused some anxiety, but with enough effort, and the encouragement of my friends, reinforced with a shot of whiskey, plus the perspective that comes with age, and a sprinkling of selective amnesia, I have come to look at those moments not too unkindly.

COMING-OF-AGE, BUT STUNTED

Secret Origins

IN THOSE TWO SCORCHING MONTHS, the summer of 1992, the most horrific events that could ever happen to a histrionic, overly dramatic kid hit me smack in the face and caused severe, irreparable whiplash. Nobody died. Nobody was diagnosed with a rare form of malignancy. Or experienced the stigmata. But things started to get sordid on the last day of fifth grade.

I was walking home from school with a five-peso cup of ice scramble when I started to feel dread swirling in my gut. In my backpack were various comic books, swapped with my classmates Ariel and Alexis, meant to be enjoyed during the summer break. The school year had just closed, and I should be enjoying a sense of liberation from my studies, the class bullies, and the tyrannical Mrs. Bahuta. While I was unpacking in my bedroom I suddenly remembered what my father and I had discussed the night before. The pieces started to fall into place, a bunch of nasty words that must be strung together. Summer. Fifth grade. Dick. Nip, nip. Suture.

There was much keening and caterwauling unbecoming of the future Dark Knight, but to my father's credit he never gave me the "*kagat ng langgam*" crap. He did give a rote account, though, of what it was like back then, with the "*labaha*", the munching on guava leaves, and the ceremonial leap to the river. Cute and quaint, but I could never understand the whole river routine. Wouldn't that give you some parasitic infection, or necrotizing penile fasciitis?

That same week the new housemaid, Tessie, arrived from a remote barrio in Bicol. She was in her early 40's, single, tall, and quite muscular. Her cropped hair was completely white. At first glance we knew she wasn't someone we could mess around with. She only needed to glare to scare the crap out of us.

In her first week, Tessie happily cooked breakfast for us. Then we promptly reverted to frying hotdogs. Her meals were not just unfamiliar or exotic, they did not make sense. Like boiled eggplant with fermented fish, sprinkled with moist rice. Or grilled fish drowned in ketchup, sprinkled with moist rice. At first we were polite, but when she served us shrimp with yellow-green sauce that was obviously not curry, I had to speak up.

"*Lasang tae*," I said. Which, predictably, made her growl, "*Talaga? Anong lasa ng tae?*"

Unlike other nanny horror stories, Tessie did not hit us on the head or brainwash us to murder our parents with a cleaver. She did, however, exhibit some strange mannerisms, such as looking up and conversing with an invisible entity hanging from the ceiling. What I hated the most was when she would dump cooked rice in her glass of cold water, then drink the blasted thing.

Tessie loved sharing superstitious tales that supposedly happened to her in the province. While gorging ourselves on Rinbee she told us how, when she was in her 20's, she found herself transported in a surreal place with pink trees, flying rocks, and frolicking fairies. These fairies ushered her into a castle, where the handsome king offered her a seat at the dining table. A dwende wearing a traditional pointed hat lined with sequins traipsed towards her carrying a plate. It had one piece of bread on it, and the bread was black. The king coaxed her to take a bite, but Tessie sensed that if she ate it, she would, of course, disintegrate. So she refused it. Or did she? She ran away from the castle, and miraculously found her way back home.

"Maybe it was just a dream," my sister said, feigning interest.

"Or a hallucination," my brother retorted.

"But it's true. I have proof," Tessie insisted.

"What proof?" we chorused.

"This!" Tessie lifted from her pocket a round object wrapped in soiled handkerchief. She unwrapped it and revealed a moldy, green-black pan de sal. The three of us laughed nervously. It was a cheap trick, but it worked. From that moment on we started listening to her stories, which usually involved paranormal phenomena.

Judging from her stories Tessie had lived one heck of a fantastic life. When she was twelve she was bitten by an aswang, and from that moment on, until she was exorcised by an albularyo, she would morph into a wild boar at midnight. When she was thirty she was cursed by a *nuno sa punso* and was shrunken. Yes, shrunken, to the size of a cockroach, for three difficult days.

"*Kasya nga ako sa mga siwang ng papag namin*," she said, beaming with pride.

The next day I developed chicken pox and grew delirious from fever. In my dream, millions of people were chasing me. The room was lined with volumes of books, which were slowly caving in. I yelled out, and at that moment I knew that it was not the run-of-the-mill nightmare. It was as though half of my consciousness was encased inside the dream, and the other half was awake. Eventually a psychiatrist would diagnose me with a common childhood medical condition called "night terrors." In the meantime, after three consecutive nights of screaming episodes, my parents decided to bring me to Niña, a woman rumored to be possessed by the spirit of the Sto. Niño.

"Stop whining," my mother said as we sat in the middle of a very stuffy room, surrounded by ten female assistants, and Sto. Niño statues in all sorts of costumes (my favorite was the one with the tennis racket). Nobody seemed to care that I could still be contagious with varicella. Niña was standing in front of a large, ornate altar, mumbling unintelligible words.

"She's starting to get possessed," my mother whispered.

Apparently, Niña was a famous healer our side of town. She was only in her 40's, and in her years of practice she had cured the usual lepers, the crippled, and the blind. She could also do psychic surgery. There was this girl, Ella, who was diagnosed with kidney cancer and had been in pain for a long time. Niña insisted that it was not cancer, that some *mambabarang* was just, of course, jealous of her good looks. According to witnesses, Niña drove her hand into Ella's abdomen and effortlessly pulled out a bunch of trash composed of eggshells, hay, ice candy plastic, granite, crumpled paper, and a decomposing cat. Since then, they claimed, the cancer-free Ella felt absolutely wonderful.

"*Ga*-graduate *na nga sya ng* nursing," said an assistant.

Presently, after uttering a bunch of prayers, Niña went into convulsions. Her eyes rolled to the back of her head, and she fell on the floor in wild, jerky spasms. But she immediately stood up, trying to fight off a full-on grand mal seizure attack.

"Who are you!" Niña shrieked as she slammed her right palm on my forehead, bursting a few chicken pox vesicles, her teeny-weeny voice like that of a castrated child's.

"Er...Will?" I whispered obediently.

"Who... are... you?" she asked again, furious.

"Will," I replied, with conviction this time.

"I cast you out! You who have been claiming this child's body, I cast you out! Now speak, what is your name?" she screamed.

Lightning, thunder, scary music.

"Will..." I insisted. What the heck could I say?

"I will make you suffer! Release this child! Admit who you are, and your penance shall be brief!" Niña wailed. My forehead started to really hurt. In the background, the disciples were droning, "Admit who you are, admit, admit, admit!"

Admit? *Admit*? I had no choice. I had to make it stop.

"Tessie," I hissed. "I am... Tessssie."

Everyone gasped audibly. Niña smiled, contented. I cried.

6

"He's crying because he's been freed," one of the disciples said with a wide, triumphant grin.

My family, along with Tessie, had dinner at Shakey's afterwards. I couldn't look at Tessie, wracked with guilt that I had borne false witness against my neighbor. Who knew what punishment the Sto. Niño had in store for her because of my lies. My parents had been advised not to let Tessie know that they "knew." The following day Niña and her disciples raided Tessie's room to look for evidence of demonic ritual, and they found spilled white paint on the floor. It was assessed to be "shaped like an evil chicken."

Evil chicken!

Judgmental Prognostications

THERE WAS A RUNNING JOKE back in med school that if you graduate at the top of your class you will become an academic or a researcher, the sort who gets published in The Lancet or the New England Journal of Medicine. You may become an author of medical textbooks, or a peer reviewer of journals who will point out fallacious conclusions from tortured statistical analyses. You will be regarded highly in the academe and invited frequently to speak, your curriculum vitae so long nobody ever volunteers to do your introduction. You will conduct clinical trials and lead research committees, your very name lending credibility to any intellectual endeavor. In your senior years, you and your small group of board exam topnotchers will start giving each other totally invented awards for excellence, service, and generally being spectacular, and you will start complaining about having so many darn trophies and laminated certificates of appreciation that take space away from your Egyptian relics.

In your tireless pursuit of excellence some aspects of your life might suffer, and you might make some horrible life choices, like marrying a total loser who doesn't know the difference between a p-value and a confidence interval. Your son might turn out to be completely ordinary, and while you tell yourself and your research-challenged wife that all that matters is your son's happiness, you also fear for how he will live his life mired in mediocrity. In your tireless pursuit of being on top you might also miss out on parties and other fun events. You won't ever get to fellate a stranger behind a dumpster in a back alley, nevertheless you are content with being cited in some newbie researcher's bibliography.

You who finish somewhere in the middle third will become successful clinicians, the sort with lines of patients waiting outside your office, with the occasional attractive pharmaceutical representatives cutting in line to give you boxes of cakes, gift baskets, trips to Switzerland, exaggerated compliments, unfunny jokes, and knick-knacks. Theoretically, you are the most well-rounded, able to juggle career, romance, family life, spirituality, and the occasional indiscretions. You are average, and proud to be.

Or at least that's what you claim. In truth you are harboring some secret sorrow for failing to live up to the high standards set by your parents, having settled for a lowly average of 2.0 and failing to snag a seat reserved for topnotchers on stage during the graduation ceremonies. Nobody really remembers the average. You are part of the crowd, the opportunity to stand out having washed away along with your youth. You compensate by hustling to earn more money, just so you can afford Hermes, Rolex, cheek implants, and abdominoplasty in time for the next annual convention, where you will see all your gaudy amigas and engage in a competition of shallowness.

And it is inevitable that the ones at the bottom, you who barely made it out of the college of medicine alive, you who always had to look at your intelligent classmates during quizzes and conferences for telepathic S.O.S, will become underground abortionists wielding clothes hangers dipped in isopropyl alcohol, illegally performing unanesthetized uterine scraping in a poorly-lit broom closet. You had your fun back in the day—parties in Ermita on a week night, risky one-night stands, long naps when you should be studying Harrison's Principles of Internal Medicine. At first you assumed that you were that rare wunderkind who can come to class without having studied a thing, and still get very high grades. You weren't. Truly your intellectual inferiority and moral ineptitude had prepared you for a long career in unsanitary abortions, or even more tragically, government service.

We first heard of these horrible, judgmental prognostications back when we were welcomed into the UP College of Medicine. They sounded totally ridiculous and too specific that they could only have been cooked up by an exquisitely bitter alumnus, but they still crept into our frantic, competitive brains. Looking around the conference hall during the freshmen orientation ceremonies, I knew that some of us would be more cut-throat than others, but nobody would want to be at the very bottom. At one point or another, all 160 of us, who had bested other contenders for subsidized medical education, would have to position ourselves in this very high, very crowded totem pole.

"Relish these five years of training. Focus on patient care. Not grades. Not competition," one of the professors said in his welcome speech. "These five years will be difficult. But the cases that you will see here will be equivalent to twenty years' worth of cases in other med schools."

We clapped to boost our prematurely inflated egos.

"But you will also look twenty years older by the time you're through."

After miserably failing the first exam (anatomy of the extremities) I was sort of getting an idea of my place in the world. I was sharing a huge classroom with geniuses, and in my head I was already straightening clothes hangers with which to fish out dead babies in the future. One such genius was this girl, Thymes. I was buying a comic book in the mall one afternoon when I saw her queueing at the ATM machine. She was reading our anatomy textbook, occasionally glancing up and murmuring to herself. She looked like she was in a trance, like she was absorbing data directly from the book, never mind that it was already her turn to withdraw. Our classmates had said that Thymes was a topnotcher in college, that she's eidetic, like the Barbara Gordon Batgirl who can memorize everything she ever lays her eyes upon. Very much unlike me, who would read something, highlight it twice, and forget it as soon as I turned the page. Thymes definitely looked like an early contender for the Researcher tier. Two of my anatomy groupmates were shoo-ins for that Researcher tier, too, for topping the board exams of their pre-med courses: Len-Len in Pharmacology, and Roxy in Physical Therapy. I heard that they had won many academic distinctions back in college, as well as a bunch of national Math and Science competitions in their youth.

Well, I also topped a very important competition once—a quiz bee on local consumerism guidelines sponsored by the Department of Trade and Industry in 1996.

A few months into med school and some average-at-best exam performances, I had given up any attempt to be excellent. I resolved that all I needed was to survive the next five harrowing years, not be involved in a scandal, and pass the board exams. Occasionally I would have attempts at sounding smart, all of which I'd regretted. I once told my anatomy groupmates, with much pomp and confidence, that I had identified an accessory spleen in our cadaver. Len-Len took one look at the structure I had marked with a red push pin and said, "I think it's just… dirt."

One of our last examinations in first year was a move-type test in Histology. You had to peer into a microscope, and in a matter of seconds try to figure out what that formalinized gunk was (A piece of ovary? A chunk of lung? Ascaris? Dirt?). I was so bad at it that I couldn't even come up with realistic guesses in some of the items. The scored answer sheets were made available a few days later, placed in a box and left in the office for everyone to see. I got 12 points out of 50, undeniably chief abortionist-level. To console myself I rummaged through the other test papers and looked for a lower score. Tommy, who always seemed so smart, got 7 out of 50. Yes! We could co-lease a poorly-lit basement clinic in the future and charge millions.

Five years of med school zipped by. We were given many diverse opportunities to prove ourselves in the world of medicine, opportunities that would one day sort us into a researcher, a clinician, or an abortionist . After we graduated, we ran to the admin office to get our class rankings. At this point we had already passed the Physician Licensure Examination. We were officially doctors of medicine, and we had our whole futures ahead of us. Still, as we opened the envelopes with our class rankings, you could hear buzzing, mumbles, cries all around:

"Abortionist ka ba? Abortionist ka ba?"

"Sino ang mga abortionists?"

"OMG abortionist ako!"

"Talaga si _____ *abortionist?* I never expected!"

"Abortionist! Abortionist! Abortionist and proud!"

A Brief History of Endorsements

IN THE OLDEN DAYS, when we were still medical students, we would flock to the conference hell—I mean hall—at 7 am, stuff our faces with turon frantically purchased from The Nosocomial Canteen, and cower in our seats. We would watch the all-mighty residents in fishnet stockings and leather boots pacing around the hall, snarling menacingly as they brandished toothed cat-o-nine tails (I have been reading a bunch of Catwoman comic books, so my memory is probably all jumbled up). The dread we felt as students during our internal medicine morning endorsements ranged from "washable with ice-cold Jeka Juice" to "get me outta here!".

In one such endorsement proceedings Intern Margie was called in front to present the previous night's ward admissions. Even as she was walking towards the podium we noticed that she was already starting to hyperventilate. This was followed by profuse sweating, until she fainted on the floor. We expected the residents to scream, "*Arte! Tumayo ka, nasa patient's name and age pa lang tayo!*", but they morphed from villainous caricatures into real people with thoughts and feelings. They ushered Margie out of the room and proceeded to give her free breakfast, instantly resolving all of her symptoms. Margie never had to endorse again during the rotation, so we stayed away from breakfast turon and tried starving ourselves. Unfortunately, none of us ever required medical evacuation.

Sometimes, after these endorsements, the resident monitor would summon us for a post-endorsement "special meeting", where he would make an impassioned speech and give an extra sprinkling of residual sermon—I mean "reminders". This post-endorsement special meeting would then be followed by a one-on-one with our residents, who would give us a list of the day's chores—or "teachable moments". A few weeks into the rotation we had become inured to all of this, most of us finding it more and more difficult to balance time between studying and doing scutwork. At this point most of us had already transformed from "I haven't finished reading about hyperglycemic hyperosmolar nonketotic coma—I am so irresponsible," into "oh what the heck!" As we were being quizzed by our chief resident, Dr. Lia, on why warfarin needs to be overlapped with heparin, we were thinking: Who cares!—which was obviously a defense mechanism because deep in our hearts we knew: The patient cares! Their loved ones care! The Hippocratic oath cares!

Ahem

Dr. Lia called us one by one. First in line was my classmate, Smoketh. She had no idea why in the world warfarin and heparin needed to be administered in overlapping schedules. It sounded like one of those algebraic word problems where you had to compute for the exact time that two leaky faucets running at different speeds would fill up those damn perforated buckets. But she knew she had to say something smart, she knew she had to maintain a veneer of intellectual curiosity, she knew that...

"Ma'am… I don't know," she said with a straight face. She then sat down. Next!

Mrs. T stood up. "Ma'am, I don't know!"

It was my turn.

"Warfarin is…. was… I don't know!"

Next in line, much to our relief, was The Talented Mr. Len-Len Chan, who knew his Harrison's Principles of Internal Medicine 16th Edition forwards, backwards, and inside-out. He gave a very succinct, spot-on answer, none of that time-buying "thank you for that wonderful question" crap, which we found so impressive that we clapped and cheered—but none louder than the clap and cheer of Chepoy Marasigan. Chepoy had been heavily perspiring and fidgeting all this time because she would have been next on the firing squad, but she was all smiles now. Sitting next to Len-Len henceforth became prime spot during endorsements.

For all the unapologetic "I-don't-knows" we had mouthed off in med school, Mrs. T, Smoketh, and I managed to slip through the cracks and got accepted into the internal medicine residency program. We became experts in all that anti-coagulation stuff, because we knew we had to care. We had to care because the patients could experience a fatal shower of embolism if we didn't do preemptive management, and we had to care because the patients would bleed if we miscalculated. We also won the right to finally wear the imaginary fishnet stockings and kinky leather boots. Initially I thought it would be titillating, but as I sat there at the other end of the table pretending to crack my invisible whip I discovered that I didn't really want to ask any question at all. Not because I was trying to ingratiate myself, but because I was too sleepy. But more importantly, because the case that my batchmate Lochia had chosen for presentation, pulmonary alveolar proteinosis, was something I hadn't encountered in real life or even read up on.

It was to Lochia's credit that at least one of us had studied the case extensively, and I decided to just let him take over the entire proceedings. My other batchmates Diana, Aids, and JD all started asking questions as well. Apparently everyone had read up on it, except me.

Intern Ericka was doing pretty well. She was confident, the patient's history was complete, it seemed that she had really performed physical examination on the patient, and she was not making any *nanette*. Nanette is the term that pertains to the act of conjuring totally made-up information from thin air, in an attempt to bluff your way out of your seniors' questions. The etymology, clearly, is Nanette Inventor. Obviously nanetting is bad, because it can adversely affect patient care. There is a rebel school of thought, however, claiming that there are details you can nanette and details you should never nanette. Whatever happens, the important thing is that you *Nanette With Conviction*. No hemming and hawing and stuttering and nervous chuckling allowed.

And just when Intern Ericka thought that she could finish unscathed, Lochia asked a question that would, one day, in post-graduate courses on Test Construction, become the prototype question on what not to ask. Lochia asked Ericka thus:

"Ericka, what laboratory finding, which, if you do not find it, will make you not consider, that it is not a diagnosis other than pulmonary alveolar proteinosis?"

Intern Ericka was momentarily stumped. She didn't know how to answer it, via Nanetting With Conviction or otherwise. Years later we would repeatedly rib Lochia about how the question didn't make any sense, but every single time Lochia would explain his cartwheeling triple-negative double flip-flop question and we would somehow get it. Somehow.

After finishing our stint in internal medicine we went our separate ways and took up different sub-specialties. Smoketh took up nephrology, Mrs. T took up rheumatology. A few days ago while whining at how horrifically dismal our lives had turned out as subspecialty fellows, Smoketh asked for my help in making internal medicine exams for students.

"*Ilang araw nga inooverlap ang warfarin and heparin? Paano nga ginagawa yun?*" Smoketh asked.

"I... I don't know," I said, and resumed reading Catwoman.

Moonlight

"PATIENT IS COMING!" Nurse Joey screamed via the two-way radio. "Patient is coming! Over!" I immediately dropped the tattered Ray Bradbury I was reading and grabbed my stethoscope. Through the tiny clinic window I saw the company golf cart rapidly emerging through the dense thicket. Nurse Annie shivered as she opened the clinic doors. She was new to this job and would get anxious whenever patients came in droves. As the captain of the ship I instructed Annie to take a deep breath and relax, things will be fine, just follow my lead. Patient was male, in his 20's, medium built. Other than caked vomit on his chin, general survey seemed unremarkable.

"What happened? What happened?" I asked, my voice stern and authoritative as I demanded for a detailed case endorsement.

"It was his fourth consecutive ride in the Twister Centrifumax Vomitron 3000," Nurse Joey said dryly, referring to the main theme park attraction. "What are we going to do, doc?"

"*Pahigain ang pasyente!*" I announced with conviction. I then went back to my cubicle and resumed reading Ray Bradbury.

Patient stood up after five minutes, a bit embarrassed, and scurried out of the clinic back into the theme park. He was in a hurry to look for the best position to get a good view of the fireworks.

"Diagnosis: Post-ride vertigo," I wrote on the chart. I never really checked if it was an official diagnosis with a corresponding international diagnostic code. I just copied the previous medical charts saying "post-ride vertigo"—which was all of them.

I was a few months into my moonlighting year when I had taken this job in the clinic of a theme park. I was not yet ready to go into residency training right after the boards, so I lounged around as a general physician for about a year. My main goals: 1) to relax and 2) to earn money. Not necessarily the loftiest for a former "*Iskolar Ng Bayan.*" But after graduating, the world suddenly seemed bigger, and nobody really cared where you had your education or how high your grades were. I would jump from one hospital to another and get paid a fee-per-duty. I revelled in the newness and the freedom of being a young physician unencumbered by structure, hierarchy, or the need to prove oneself.

In the summer my friends and I went on duty in a Boracay clinic which caters to locals and tourists. I had taken the job with much apprehension—I didn't have a lot of clinical experience just yet and internet was not as ubiquitous. Good thing I had my trusty Palm Pilot and all sorts of tickler notebooks where we had jotted down notes on how to manage STD's, ear infections, alcohol intoxication, and mishaps involving sea urchins.

"Cast all your fears aside," my friend Chepoy Marasigan said during the orientation. "Whatever knowledge you need is already deep inside your brain… and in your heart." Whereas I would only be going on duty in the island for about two weeks, Chepoy had been staying there for months, having fallen in love with the island lifestyle and the state of zen it had afforded her. In the morning, she would perform minor surgeries and bring stroke patients to nearby cities aboard a helicopter. At night she would party and fall in love.

"Besides," she whispered. "The most important skill is to make *chika* to the highest level to all patients. No uncomfortable silences, no tapping of pens while waiting for lab results, no pretending that there's an emergency phone call you have to take." Being an untrained schizoid, this sounded way more intimidating than the lack of clinical skills. Still, I found myself getting surprisingly gregarious on many occasions, aided by the spirit of the island and a few shots of alcohol. One particularly tiring night, though, I was totally spent and had no small talk left in me. The clinic head had sent me to a hotel room belonging to a European woman who had injured herself while cutting lemons for a cocktail. My mission was to administer the anti-tetanus shots.

"Thanks for cleaning my *vound*. How long do we have to *vait* for the skin test?" she asked.

"Around thirty minutes," I gulped. The prospect of having to make small talk in English for thirty minutes filled me with horror. She hadn't taken that cocktail yet, and she was starting to get uncomfortable with the silence as well.

"So," she snickered.

"So," I snickered back.

"So," she repeated.

And then, I finally had a bright idea, because we still had twenty-five minutes of silence that desperately required a bright idea.

"How long have you been in Boracay?" I asked.

"Two *veeks!*"

"*Vonderful,*" I cheerily said. "Can you tell me all the activities that you've had so far?" And thus were 30 minutes consumed.

I was down to my last few duties in the theme park, as I had finally been accepted in a residency training program. The timing couldn't have been more perfect—my clinical skills had completely stalled in the past year, my diagnostic abilities limited to post-ride vertigo or island hook-up-induced gonorrhea. I was ready to jump in and become a slave in the hospital bureaucracy once more. It was time.

To get accepted in a residency program, I had to undergo two weeks of pre-residency hospital exposure, something akin to a live reality competition where I needed to outshine all the other applicants. I chose a 3-year residency training in internal medicine, or I.M. Everyone was intense and competitive, and there was always an implicit wish that the other applicants would get disillusioned, go into brief reactive psychosis, and quit, freeing up a slot. If I didn't know any better, I would suspect that in one of my ward duties another applicant, Hilda, deliberately stole the prescriptions I had already filled-up just to drive me bonkers.

One night while resting in the quarters with my duty partner, Jobert, a senior doctor walked by. He asked us what residency training program we were applying for. Jobert quipped, rather morosely, "I.M., sir." As soon as the senior doctor left, Jobert's mood shifted and his eyes turned glassy, as if divine realization had smacked him on the face.

"I.M…" Jobert whispered.

"What?" I asked from the upper bunk of the bed.

"I.M… I.M…" Jobert droned on. "I.M… I am quitting."

Jobert stood up and drove away in the middle of the night, never to be seen again.

On my last duty day in the theme park Nurse Joey brought in patient Suzie, 30 years old, at around 4 PM. She had suffered severe vertigo after being spun, tossed around, and hurled backwards while hanging upside down. Nurse Annie and I welcomed her in the clinic. A few months into the routine Nurse Annie had become quite confident in her arduous task of opening the door with grace. By necessity she really had to exhibit leadership qualities. I was about to leave, and Nurse Joey was already finalizing his documents for Saudi.

"*Pahigain ang pasyente!*" I declared with gusto, like an actor over-acting his way into the final performance of a long theatrical run. I was about to resume reading Philip K. Dick when Suzie's friends barged-in and approached me in panic.

"Hi, where is Dr. Suzie is she okay? Is she dyspneic?"

"Yes I asked her to lie down, I think she's having, um, post-ride vertigo."

Wait, did she just use the word "dyspneic"?

"Is her heartbeat regular? Did she complain of any anginal chest pains?", one of them asked. "Suzie is a doctor from Manila Medical Institute And Training Hospital For Excellence. We are also doctors. She has a history of atrial fibrillation, but she still insisted on taking the ride. We don't have her list of meds. Did you auscultate her? She has a history of Graves' Disease. I think she even stopped taking her meds a few weeks ago. She's also been having irregular menses but she refused to take a pregnancy test. What should we do, doc, what should we do?"

"Uhm… uhm…"

"I think she's been on chronic anti-coagulation," concerned doctor friend went on. "I think we have to examine if there were any signs of bleeding, or if…"

Damn it.

Bludgeonella's Bludgeonings

SMOKETH HAS RECENTLY SEEN our beloved mentor Dr. Riahnna Bludgeonella in a bakery buying empanada. Years after we had trained under her the mere mention of her name still triggers fear and intense feelings of inadequacy. As apprehensive, sniveling first year residents back then we all trembled whenever there was news that she would go on rounds at the intensive care unit. We mistakenly assumed once that no consultant ever goes to the hospital on a Good Friday, and that we could just watch a couple of DVD's to drown out the eerie combination of silence and noise in the ICU.

My senior resident Kate glowered at me when she caught me reading a comic book. She told me to study my patients, specifically Mrs. E.M. who was suffering from a terrible case of heart failure and pneumonia. It had been weeks since she was brought to the ICU, and we still couldn't wean her off the ventilator. She was fully conscious, alert, and at that point totally infuriated, her eyes rolling in resigned annoyance whenever a nurse would suction her endotracheal tube. The repeated needle pricks and ventilator manipulation that had once caused her to wince or cry now only aggravated her impatience. At one point she managed to loosen her restraints and tried to pull out the endotracheal tube herself, much to our horror. It was therefore a good thing, a fantastic thing, that Dr. Riahnna Bludgeonella had chosen to grace us with her presence and save us from the follies of amateurishness.

Even though I was already in the mindset that I was a prokaryote who knew absolutely nothing, I never really found myself prepared for the blunt force trauma to the ego that only Dr. Riahnna Bludgeonella could administer. Her first pick for presentation: my patient Mrs. E.M. She started asking questions about her history, and I immediately got flustered because all my patients had a similar profile: thin, elderly women with hypertension, diabetes, tuberculosis, pneumonia, and respiratory failure. Even as I was rattling off the details of the case I was starting to doubt if I hadn't mixed everybody up.

"Why is she still intubated?" she finally asked.

I mumbled.

"You don't know? You've been handling this patient for two weeks now, and still…"

When my senior Kate sensed that survival mode was starting to kick in, and that I was about to desperately Nanette Inventor my way through the rounds, she pushed me aside and answered the questions herself.

"I don't think we can extubate the patient just yet, because frankly, I am not yet comfortable given the clinical parameters. If we look at the X-ray…" Kate spoke in confident English as she slapped the X-ray film against the viewing lamp. Dr. Riahnna Bludgeonella stared at Kate for a few seconds, as though making a full assessment of her character and integrity. She then leaned back, crossed her arms, and smiled, very much content with Kate's response. It was quite an umbrella statement if I may say so myself, but with her grace, conviction, and diction, Kate had saved the day magnificently. After putting us through the wringer for three hours Dr. Riahnna gave us her recommendations on how to best manage the patient's respiratory failure. In a few days the patient was successfully extubated.

Fast forward to two years later. I was already a senior resident like the graceful Kate was before me, and I was now in charge of the ICU. I had always hoped that I could one day emulate the intellectual and emotional maturity that Kate had exhibited. I realized that I would soon be put to the test when news came that Dr. Riahnna Bludgeonella would be making her ICU rounds that afternoon. In my team was the first year resident Jukelya Mae, who was quite the promising newbie. Dr. Riahnna threw open the swinging doors of the ICU, and the interns and nurses scuttled away in panic. Like a high school principal during PAASCU accreditation I quickly told Jukelya Mae, with a hint of disdain for her lack of initiative, to carry Dr. Riahnna's gigantic hand bag. I greeted her with ingratiating fondness, which, in retrospect, must have seemed completely irritating. She wasn't in the mood for niceties. Earlier she had caused two junior residents to run out of the wards in tears, and Jukelya Mae was destined to be the third if I, her senior, wouldn't be able to save her.

Jukelya Mae started endorsing her patient, Mr. T.D., an encephalopathic 50 year-old-male with small cell lung cancer, pericardial effusion, drug-induced neutropenia, and hospital acquired pneumonia. It was Jukelya's first week in residency, and she was obviously starting to panic. Dr. Riahnna Bludgeonella let out an audible sneer at the report that the patient had been hooked to the ventilator for two weeks now, and that Jukelya Mae couldn't successfully wean him out. In what I thought was a glorious full circle moment, I tapped Jukelya Mae on the shoulder, pushed her aside, and murmured "let me".

"I don't think we can extubate the patient just yet, because I am not yet comfortable given the clinical parameters," I uttered with conviction. Kate would be proud of me, I thought. And I was quite pleased with myself—first for actually remembering Kate's umbrella statement, and second, for finding this exact opportunity to save someone with something that had saved me before. I waited for Dr. Riahnna Bludgeonella to happily lean back and heap me praises. You've learned so much in two years, she would say. The growth in confidence is astronomical. Like a fabulous phoenix, you've…

"You're not yet comfortable?" Dr. Riahnna Bludgeonella growled. "I don't care if you're not yet comfortable! Is anybody here concerned about your comfort? This is not about your comfort! You think the patient cares about your comfort? You think…"

I looked around. Kate was no longer there to save me. My failed, overeager attempt to demonstrate leadership amplified the embarrassment.

Moral lesson: there's no such thing as symmetry, full circle, or comfort levels.

Pure Nanette

SENIOR CONSULTANT DR. AMBROSIO MAXIMO, with his authoritative heft and characteristic scowl, towered mightily over me at the nurse's station on the 4th floor. It was the morning after my 24-hour duty in the pay floors, and as soon as I was summoned, I knew I was in for a very public lashing. I hadn't brushed my teeth yet, so my fetid breath must have further irritated him, making him turn redder by the minute. He was, at that point, ready to bite my head off and spit it out the window straight into a medical waste disposal unit. I didn't know exactly what I had done wrong, but as lowly first year residents festering at the bottom of the totem pole we had gotten used to getting the third degree for just about anything.

Behind the furious Dr. Maximo stood Nurse Trixie, who was trying her best—and miserably failing—not to snicker. To make it seem like she was not eavesdropping she pretended that she was dusting off imaginary breadcrumbs on her shirt, then stacking together patient charts on the counter. I then remembered that at around 4 am she had referred to me the laboratory test results of Dr. Maximo's patient. In the middle of explaining the results to the patient's daughter, I got another call for something urgent. I immediately left and ran to the other wing, saying that I would be back. That was my only interaction with any of Dr. Maximo's patients during my tour of duty, so maybe I had offended the relative in some way.

Dr. Maximo's booming voice caught the attention of everyone in the hallway, and soon people were flocking around, pretending that they were texting or doing chart rounds. Like all the other residents I was used to getting scolded, but this time I felt like the reprimands were disproportionate to my crime. Dr. Maximo went on to accuse me of being arrogant, insubordinate, and an absolute diva who could not be bothered to attend to his patients. Soon, totally unrelated issues were getting dredged up: "Do you want to be like some of my colleagues," he yelled, "who have no patients because they are so full of themselves? Why are you dressed like that? You don't look like a doctor, have you tried applying for a non-medical job?" And my favorite: "What was your class rank in med school?"

I silently shook my head.

"Oh really, you don't know?"

I shook my head again, wishing I could answer back: I know my rank, but I refuse to say it as an arrogant, insubordinate diva!

"You're an abortionist, aren't you? Aren't you?"—I imagined him saying. He must be one of those who had perpetuated those judgmental prognostications.

A few more synonyms of "arrogant", "insubordinate", and "pure evil" later, Dr. Maximo ordered me to get out of his face. I walked away in relief, but before I could even get to the staircase he immediately called me back. Maybe he would somehow apologize for being too harsh, I thought. Of course I wouldn't make it too hard for him. Of course I would exhibit magnanimity, and at the same time make it seem like I wasn't too affected by his reprimands which were definitely meant to be constructive. These tiny misunderstandings happen, after all. Some things get lost in translation when written on the chart, or when relayed by the staff, or...

He did not call me to apologize. He resumed the bashing bonanza, and, not quite satisfied with his castigations, listed five diseases on a prescription pad. He told me to read up and report on them, in that exact nurses' station, the very next day. I was hoping he would just ask for a reflection paper.

Seeing me getting all crestfallen, and quite puzzled at that unfortunate incident, my supportive batchmates went on full investigative journalism/chika mode. Their final reportage: Nurse Trixie had informed Dr. Maximo that it took me an hour to see his patient, and that when I did, I was scowling and raising my voice in annoyance. The relative then supposedly cried—cried!—because I ran away screaming like a maniac. Which was easily verifiable. So whether or not there was a Temporary Restraining Order I sneaked back into the patient's room. I was starting to doubt that maybe I had been nasty and deserving of the verbal lashings. I asked the relative if I offended her that morning. She had no idea what I was talking about.

Pure Nanette!

One of the witnesses to the public shaming, senior fellow Dr. Emily Mae Eleganza, caught me in the elevator and gave the nicest, kindest, most inspirational words of commiseration: "She is a two-faced monster, avoid her at all cost!" Apparently, Nurse Trixie had been quite infamous for chronically inflating her importance or completely making-up stories that had gotten so many trainees in the past decade into trouble.

Still, from that day on, I would always be looking across hallways and peering through peepholes just to make sure that I wouldn't cross paths with Dr. Maximo. I would subtly make a U-turn to avoid him on the floors, or more efficiently, I would hide behind a portable x-ray machine or a water cooler. Upon the advice of my friend Smoketh I started donning, as a disguise, an N-95 mask and cheap decorative eyeglasses. I thought I was being sneaky and smart, but a month later what I had been dreading finally happened: Dr. Maximo was assigned as our charity service consultant, and I was required to directly report to him twice a week.

"Hi Dr. Maximo, these are the members of our team, Will and Lovelle," our service senior Dr. Lou said.

"Oh, hi Will! Hi, Lovelle!" Dr. Maximo said.

Throughout our first service rounds Dr. Maximo was smiling, laughing, joking, and telling us that we were doing great. That we were just the best. Still trying to keep up appearances of being nice and jolly, eh, I thought miserably. At the prodding of Dr. Lou, I once had to personally see him in his office to endorse a difficult case, and he was still smiling, laughing, joking and telling me I was doing a fantastic job. Strangely I did not sense any veiled hostility, or any recognition for that matter. Or maybe he was planning a long con, trying to make me writhe in morbid anticipation, luring me into complacency so he could spring a surprise act of retribution. At the end of the rotation he gave us his evaluation forms. He gave me a score of 100%. In all this I was no longer wearing a disguise. He must have forgiven me for my sins.

"Or your worsening acne must have been enough of a disguise," Lovelle later told me.

"You really think so?" I asked, a bit hurt, as I touched my greasy face with my sweaty, filthy palms.

"Yeah, the pustules are getting a bit…"

I get it, Lovelle, no need to belabor the point. I'm going to the derma.

Misadventures in Merville

AFTER HOURS OF RUNNING WET like extras in a disaster movie, the seven of us had finally found refuge in a stranger's house in Merville. We deserved to be in that predicament because none of us had listened—we were too exhilarated to leave the hospital that nobody was remotely sane. There were twenty-one of us in our internal medicine residency batch, each one fairly smart with impressive credentials, and yet no one had the sense to admit that braving a huge storm for a beach party was a terrible idea.

Once a year, each batch of internal medicine residents was granted a weekend off for rest, recreation, and debauchery. A few weeks leading to it that was all we could yak about—we had transformed into grade 4 students who would lose sleep over the scheduled trip to the Coke plant and The Planetarium. The other internal medicine residents would be covering for us, we would have breakfast in full view of the sea, and our phones would be free of any referrals for dyspnea, diarrhea, and a heart rate of 103 beats per minute.

By the time we left PGH there was already a downpour, but nobody cared. The previous night others had driven ahead to the resort, and they had been sending us pictures of such fun and relaxation. "I'm sure in a few minutes the rain will stop," our batch head Loreta declared as she loaded her things into the trunk. Kathy was driving the SUV, and with us were Janet, Lloydie, Fulet, and Tessie. By 9 am we were ready to leave, but the rain was getting worse.

"This rain is so bad," Kathy said, who seemed to be finally coming to her senses. "Guys do you think… do you think we should go to Nasugbu, or La Luz?"

"La Luz!" we chorused.

For three seconds we actually thought we would get there unscathed. "*Tumigil na ang ulan!*" I screamed crazily, and everyone applauded, until we realized that we were only shielded from the rain by an overpass. On the radio, news was coming in that this typhoon was much more horrific than anyone had anticipated in terms of rainfall, and that many areas in Metro Manila were also starting to get deluged. They were calling the typhoon Ondoy. We hung our heads in shame and only admitted what total morons we were by the time water was sloshing into the SUV.

"Let's get out *na*," Kathy said with surprising calmness, as she pulled up the handbrake and grabbed her bag. We immediately jumped out of the car and ran through the flood along South Luzon Expressway opposite the direction of the traffic, noting that everyone had started doing the same. It was a scene out of Deep Impact or Godzilla or any B-movie minus the rampaging eight-legged creature feature. Of course we were all in summer wear. Loreta's top was thin, flowy, and white, perfect for walking introspectively along the beaches of San Juan to the tune of From A Distance. With a few drops of rain it turned in to a transparent magic *kamison*.

"*Potang pekpek shorts 'to!*" she screamed as we waded through the rapidly rising floodwaters. Of course, no one could let that near-drowning opportunity pass—we saw an elevated area and posed for disaster photography behind a chicken-wire fence. Misery is temporary and should therefore be memorialized.

The 7-Eleven in Merville was crowded with people clawing at each other for that last piece of pepperoni hotdog in the warmer. We took shelter in a corner outside the store, teeth chattering, shivering in our wet clothes, slapping ourselves for being total idiots, imagining how comfortable the hospital must be right now. The brunt of the storm had passed, and there was only a slight drizzle at this point. Tessie crossed the street at the risk of more flood water exposure and got all of us some doxycycline capsules for leptospirosis prophylaxis. Everyone in 7-11 was calling everyone on their cellphones—some worried sick about their loved ones, others asking about their properties, but most importantly, everyone was trying to compete with each other on who was having a more miserable time.

"I'm eating wet hotdog on a stick!" Janet told Alanis Cornucopia on the phone.

"Well, I only have one bag of chips, to share with everyone!" Alanis Cornucopia said. She was in the other car with Mars and Ruter, their group stuck in a parking lot in BGC.

"A firetruck just zoomed by because there's a huge fire in the village, right this moment!" Janet screamed. "Is there fire in BGC? Is there?"

One of our batchmates, Jondi, who was already in Batangas since the previous night, informed us that he knew a family living in Merville. They would let us stay the night. After a season's worth of reality TV misadventures such as getting in the wrong house, staying under the recurrent rain for hours, getting entranced by an electrical conflagration, failing to complete a Road Block because it's a task that only one member of the team may perform, contracting botulism, and such, we finally found the house. We were afraid the owners would require us to declaim "alms, alms," in the rain before letting us in, but they were extremely nice and accommodating. While dining on corned beef and rice over candlelight, we were subtly trying to assess just how close Jondi was with them. I asked them how they knew Jondi.

"Umm, yeah, si Dondee," the super nice mom told us, stammering a bit. "*Oo, oo... mabait na bata yang si Dondee.*"

To our small contingent's credit everyone was still funny and in high spirits despite the lingering stress, but I ran out of any punchlines by the time it was dark.

"*Magpatawa ka,*" Lloydie demanded.

"*Naubusan na ako,*" I whimpered.

Prior to being fed, I had asked Fulet, in sheer hunger, "Hey Fulet, have you seen the movie Alive, about the plane crash in the Andes? The passengers were stuck with each other and they had no food and they started eating each other?"

"You've already told that story 30 minutes ago," she said drily.

Kathy's mother fetched us the following morning. I went back to my boarding house and saw all kinds of trash that had been dumped in by the flood. Helliza called to say that they found catfish on the grounds outside the university library. We then learned of all the destruction the typhoon had brought—the seven of us had a misadventure, a mini-ordeal, a cute anecdote that we could later on laugh about, but many had heartbreaking tragedies. As we would learn in about two weeks, more tragedies were to come, as the emergency rooms would start to get swamped by patients who were jaundiced, anuric, and hemorrhaging from leptospirosis.

Into The Knacker

PATIENT CALOY WAS BROUGHT to the emergency room some three nights ago, and since then we had been struggling to find a vacant bed for him at the intensive care unit. He was initially hauled in by jail officers, writhing and moaning, his wrists in handcuffs. At first, he merely seemed inebriated, until he started gasping and fell into a coma.

It was one of the worst times in recent memory to be coming to the PGH emergency room. The recent wave of leptospirosis brought about by Ondoy had prompted the hospital staff to set up patient beds and nurse stations along hallways and auditoriums, transforming them into some kind of ER-ICU-Ward hybrid. Many patients coming in were "turfed" to nearby hospitals, and those who were eventually admitted on account of their life-threatening conditions had to compete with the jaundiced leptospirosis patients coughing out blood.

By the time I went on duty, Caloy's condition had completely deteriorated. For three days now he'd been stuck in the critical area of the emergency room hooked to a mechanical ventilator, all sorts of contraptions, and a bevy of IV bottles. Nobody could figure out the root cause of his condition, and at this point he was already burning up from aspiration pneumonia. Syrupy phlegm was gushing out through his endotracheal tube. His chest was covered with coagulated blood admixed with encrusted phlegm, smearing the face of the woman tattooed on his moist skin.

"Forty eight-year-old male in the acute care unit, encephalopathy multifactorial, aspiration pneumonia, negative for lepto, no definitive neurologic diagnosis yet..." Fulet Esplana rattled off. "Follow-up two units of blood, follow-up cultures, follow-up vacancy in the ICU, inform neurology, pulmonology, infectious disease, general medicine that the patient is still in the ER... and most importantly this patient does not have any *bantay*!"

Caloy had *bantays* all right—the police officers standing guard outside the emergency room. Given the state of the hospital at the time, one of the most vital elements in a patient's survival was having a very efficient companion. I wanted to tell the officers: since Caloy does not seem to have any relatives around, how about you gentlemen donate blood, or go to the cashier to pay for these diagnostic tests, or volunteer to suction the profuse secretions, or at least tell us something that can help us make an accurate diagnosis? How about that?

"They won't do anything," Fulet Esplana explained. "They're just standing outside. Sometimes they take cigarette breaks. They are only here to make sure that our comatose patient won't extubate himself, run to Taft Avenue, and take a bus to Cavite."

Caloy had no one around and understandably so. According to the triage officer he was serving time for raping his two kids. While in prison he had developed bizarre behavior, such as sprinkling cigarette ash on his soup, or picking a random fight with a known murderer. He had also developed fever and diarrhea. Also seizures. Or maybe he was just shivering? No known toxic ingestion. He was supposedly seen guzzling something in a brown bottle a few days prior. Was it just beer? Or was it beer laced with poison? Nobody could really get a decent history. In an attempt to contribute something I looked for the two gentlemen to make a bit of chit chat and maybe gather some useful information. They were nowhere to be found.

There was nothing else we could do for him at the emergency room, and the ER Officer was already foaming at the mouth for our inability to transfer him out. I had used up all my friendship cards, and she wanted the patient moved out of the emergency room now. Fawning and begging finally got me somewhere, as the charge nurse finally bequeathed me a bed in the wards. We were about to wheel him out (a major feat I could be proud of during the morning endorsements) when two women arrived and asked for some time with him.

"He is GCS 3," I explained, referring to the patient's state of consciousness, with 15 points being fully awake, and 3 points indicating total, unarousable coma. "He barely breathes on his own. Only the medications are keeping his blood pressure up."

One of the women started whispering to Caloy's ear, weeping heavily. I left them so I could attend to the other patients, mostly with leptospirosis of different levels of severity. Sitting on his stretcher seemingly bored out of his wits was patient C.E., a 19-year-old tricycle driver who almost drowned somewhere in Marikina during Ondoy. Other than fever he seemed fine. There was a yellow flag hanging by the IV stand on his stretcher.

"What the hell is this?" I asked my co-resident Diana.

"It's the new color-coding scheme to categorize the severity of leprospirosis. I think yellow means very severe leptospirosis because it's the color of jaundice. Or is it... mild leptospirosis, because very severe things are supposed to be red?"

The following morning our chairman Dr. ADM would berate us for coming up with all kinds of useless schemes in dealing with this public health crisis. She was right, because nobody really cared about those darn flags.

"That is Caloy's wife, an employee in a cellphone store in Quiapo," Nurse Muriel whispered while I was inserting an IV line on another patient. Even though the emergency room, with its rapid influx of patients, was not conducive to taking detailed personal and social history, the number of eavesdroppers somehow filled-in the gaps. "She was whispering to his ear that she forgives him. She has already talked to a lawyer. They decided to sign a waiver to bring him home where he can die in peace."

Explaining the Home Against Medical Advice form and what she could expect in-transit took me fifteen minutes. The wife promptly signed it and wept some more. I offered to refer her to psychiatry to help her in processing what should be a very complex emotional burden, but she just wanted to go home with her husband. Nurse Muriel started removing the foley catheter, the inotrope drips that were keeping his blood pressure up, the cardiac monitor pads. I told the wife that the endotracheal tube connecting him to the ventilator would be pulled out once everything was ready. She had already arranged for transportation to pick them up. "I hope they at least have a tank with an oxygen mask in the vehicle," I said.

"The wife can't bring him home!" Policeman Bruno insisted, suddenly emerging from his cigarette, iced-tea, cheeseburger, ice cream, and gossip break. "He is still a prisoner. Caloy goes back to prison with us!"

Policeman Ton-Ton agreed, droning "yes, yes, yes".

"He is a rapist! A criminal! Justice! Justice!" Policeman Bruno screamed with indignation.

"Have you seen him?" I whined, unable to hide the cartwheeling of my eyeballs. "His BP is dropping quickly. He is comatose,"

"But he might escape," Sir Bruno said. Nurse Muriel and I almost burst out laughing but managed to stop ourselves, because you know, we had to respect the authorities and all that.

"As soon as we unhook him from the ventilator, his breathing will get compromised. Then his heart," I explained with condescending slowness.

"But he might…"

"Do you have a doctor on duty tonight in prison? If he suddenly stops breathing while he is in the police patrol car, will you turn around and bring him back here…"

Officers Bruno and Ton-Ton must have gotten tinnitus from my rants which were getting more high-pitched by the minute, that they decided to pick up their two-way radio to confer with their senior officers. Also, it was already 4 am.

Patient Caloy had been unhooked from the ventilator for almost five minutes now, and to our surprise, he was still breathing shallowly on his own. If he suddenly stood up and ran to the bus station I would probably be charged for being an accessory to something. His blood pressure was quickly dropping, now down to 80 palpatory. His wife told us the transportation should be arriving by now.

Finally, at the break of dawn, their car service made a complete stop in front of the emergency room. I was expecting a private or barangay ambulance with in-transit resuscitation capabilities. Or at least a working siren. Instead, what arrived was a huge private van, with a sign painted on it: Santo Benigno Funeral Homes.

The wife turned to me and murmured, "thank you, thank you, thank you, thank you…" before promptly taking the front seat of the van.

"But…" Nurse Muriel whimpered.

The van furiously sped away.

All Because of That Damn Chalupa

"ATTENTION!" JD ANNOUNCED in the call room. "Will is hypotensive and he is going to die!"

Such sensationalism might have seemed unnecessary for an isolated determination of a vasovagal 80/60, but JD knew that it would require cheap shock value to reach the sleepy and the weary. He had taken my blood pressure after seeing me retching and bent over on the mattress, and everyone would have readily believed him, too, had he not been snickering the whole time. "Let's insert an intravenous line for hydration! His BP is down! He's in pain! This is not a joke! Why are you laughing, Gracie! Get an IV stand!"

It all started with a mild abdominal pain in the middle of my ER duty. I assumed that it was just "dyspepsia with alarm" from all the missed meals and alcoholism, so I forced myself to gorge on a piece of chalupa overloaded with chunks of chorizo. I then vomited said chunks of chorizo, and writhed on the bed clutching my tummy.

It was already 10 pm. There were five of us in the quarters, and everyone was taking a break from their duty posts. 10 pm had always been the best time for the residents-on-duty to have dinner or a quick nap. It coincided with the nurses' endorsements, during which all the patient charts were walled-off. Before the transition to electronic medical records the battle for possession of the patients' ER charts was an intense political game involving lots of chasing and subterfuge. The residents wanted to write their orders, the nurses wanted to carry them out, the interns wanted to write their notes so they could get the hell out of there, the ER officer wanted to write admonitions that the patients were overstaying. At the height of this craziness, I once found a patient's chart stashed inside a hollowed-out CPU of an old desktop computer, which also begged the question of what happened to the physical contents of that CPU. Come endorsement time at 10 pm, however, the nurses were untouchably supreme, and the charts rightfully belonged to them. In these fleeting moments of forced respite, the last thing anybody wanted was the inconvenience of a co-resident dropping dead.

Upon hearing this grim public service announcement, and realizing that I was indeed on the throes of death, Ren immediately pulled my hand and fished for my turgid, wriggling veins. When the needle was inserted Marth secured blood samples for diagnostics. My blood pressure immediately shot back to normal when JD offered/threatened to bring me to the emergency room. Just outside the door there was an aluminum stretcher that we had used to haul in boxes of donated medicines. It would be easy enough to toss me into the stretcher, and with a vigorous kick send me flying straight into triage.

"I would rather go on duty in this state of abject misery and pain!" I protested with self-entitled indignation, eyes bleary, post-vomit spittle dangling from the corners of my mouth. JD then pushed some delectable, powerful pain relievers into my intravenous port, quickly ending my infernal whining.

"We've been telling you to have your gallbladder taken out since last year!" he cheerily nagged.

I woke up in a daze the next day, the cacophony of my batchmates' early morning endorsements and breakfast gossip announcing that I was still in the residents' callroom, still very much alive. While everyone was blabbering, I pulled out the IV line and sneaked out of the quarters, like a patient absconding from the hospital for unpaid bills. My batchmates would later discover the unhooked IV line left lying on the bed, residual fluid dribbling from the macroset tubings, abandoned by a difficult, over-dramatic patient who had survived another intense gallstone attack. For years I had promised myself that I would never have my beleaguered gallbladder taken out, until such time that I am bright yellow, febrile, and totally septic. But now, in the face of becoming the center of unwanted attention, ie., *pabigat*, my resolve was starting to crumble. How easy it is to make these silly pronouncements, until we are faced with the very real prospect of discomfort, death, and disfigurement.

"There they are… swirling around," my friend Roma said as she gently pressed the ultrasound probe on my abdomen. Through the years of repeated ultrasounds, I had heard them all—that it was a baby boy, that it was just feces, or that I was secretly harboring a shriveled-up uterus so I better get that karyotype done immediately. Noting my anxiety this time, Roma decided to skip the stand-up routine. "If it's painful you should see surgery immediately! That's basic second year med student knowledge!" she said. There and then, with my huge belly exposed and glistening from too much KY jelly, I asked the favorite question of the typical Pinoy patient, something that I never thought I would ask: "*Wala bang pampatunaw ng bato?*"

That night, alone in my room, my abdomen started acting up again. I imagined the stones bumping into each other, grating against the gallbladder walls with their jagged edges, like living creatures trying to burst out. Everyone assumes that these stones cause pain when they crowd their way through a narrow exit point, but my attacks always felt like the stones were actively slicing and slashing through the walls. What if they're ascaris, I thought. What if there's a tumor?

I quickly rummaged through my stash of emergency medications and found two ampules of tramadol. I tied a handkerchief on my left arm, and with my teeth pulled the edge to tighten it, something I learned from Trainspotting and Requiem For a Dream. With my free hand I injected the needle into an engorged vein, but without meaning to I slightly pulled the plunger, aspirating some blood. Before I knew it, a significant amount of blood had rushed into the syringe, cocktailing with the tramadol. Panicking, I dropped the syringe, and blood squirted all over the bed. I quickly removed the handkerchief, cursing myself for being a total idiot. I prepared a fresh dose, careful not to spill it. If I botched it I would have to walk all the way to the drug store, bent over and whimpering, hoping I were on a dilapidated aluminum stretcher.

I injected the drug directly into my arm muscle this time. I did not have any upper arm musculature to speak of, and the needle nicked the bone. "*Pota!*" I screamed.

My conclusion: I need to work out.

While waiting for my surgery I remembered the urban legend that sometimes, anesthetized patients still feel the incisions during the procedure, but they can't scream. And that they can still hear the gossips, the judgmental remarks, and the conspiratorial whispers of the surgical team, but are too paralyzed to object. At this point I was just going through a checklist of things that an anxious patient is wont to do, such as terrorizing oneself with all these online rumors. Other items in the checklist included complaining to the nurse multiple times that my "dextrose" had stalled and asking if I could skip the foley catheter. I couldn't.

As I was strapped on the operating table, I told myself that I would try to resist falling asleep from the general anesthesia, just to see if I could. As soon as the rubber mask landed on my face, I rested my eyes for one second, opened them, and then heard someone say, "*Tapos na po!*" It was the scrub nurse, wheeling me out of the operating room and into recovery.

A few friends visited me on my second post-operative day. The last time I saw them was a few years ago, when we attended the wedding of a high school classmate. I started to wonder if visiting each other in the hospital would now be standard fare for our age, our regular activity, in place of "debut" birthdays, engagement parties, and weddings. Or if not visiting each other in the hospital, maybe visiting our sick, aging parents. At the time, my dad was still responding very well to his oral cancer medications, well enough that he and my mother had volunteered to be my watchers during my confinement. But there was always the foresight that his cancer would soon progress, and my mother had wisely pushed me to have this surgery before that time comes.

I was able to go back to work after a weekend of rest. I had hoped that I would still be suffering from some post-operative pain so I could justify a longer leave, but there was nothing there, only the imagined emptiness from a relatively minor evisceration. I walked into the wards and saw familiar faces, and for a moment there I expected some kind of a welcome party. Or at the very least a silent acknowledgment, a half-smile, a knowing look, or a nod, so as not to interrupt regular hospital operations in my behalf. It was like the laparoscopic cholecystectomy had earned me a sense of superiority, a feeling that I had survived something and you should take note of it, because what have you survived recently? And in the PGH wards it was a ridiculous question to ask. This sense of entitlement thankfully fizzled quickly enough, saving me from the embarrassment of walking with a fake limp for attention.

And just when I had accepted that there was to be no transitory event, and I had finally snapped back into a full-on resident-on-duty mode, I saw my batchmate Lochia going on rounds in the same ward. From the other end of the corridor he yelled, "Congratulations! *Operada ka na!*" The nurses and med students looked at me. One even gave a perfunctory "OMG are you okay!" I flashed a half-smile and went back to work.

BRP

IN THE MIDDLE OF GETTING FITTED for our PGH Internal Medicine bomber jacket Smoketh remarked that I was getting quite svelte and that my arms had become shockingly thin. Must be the gallbladder surgery, I said, still trying to remind everyone that I had gone through something important. To return the compliment I told her that I've always envied her broad shoulders. Standing behind me, eavesdropping, was Lochia, who said that not all women would appreciate such an insensitive comment.

In an attempt to make up for this tactlessness I quickly followed it up with an anecdote that happened in the residents' quarters a few weeks back. It was about my physical insecurities and would explain my desire to have firm upper body musculature. If it seemed like it was too much of an elaborate, unnecessary bother for a supposed apology, it was because I also wanted someone to listen to my sordid tale of abuse and self-pity. Smoketh and Lochia had nowhere else to go, trapped in the fitting room as my captive audience.

It all started one afternoon in the residents' callroom when we noticed our batchmate, Lilandra Marie, scowling and typing furiously on her laptop. We asked her if she wanted to have chilled taho with us, but she just dismissed us with a grunt. Through the keyboard clacks Alanis Cornucopia whispered that Lilandra Marie had been in a foul mood the past few days. Lilandra Marie's desk was located in the corner just beside the door, and ever since the doorknob got jammed all we ever did was bitch and whine about it. There were twenty-one of us coming and going through that door, and every single day Lilandra Marie had to endure our complaints like a telepath who couldn't shut off other people's thoughts. Whines unleashed while dealing with the doorknob ranged from a simple, grating "tsk!" to an existential "Of course this doorknob is busted too. Of course!" Lilandra Marie had become the unintended recipient of all our existential angst. Meanwhile, no one had volunteered to actually fix the damn door.

"Poor Lilandra Marie," I told Alanis Cornucopia. Sensing what I was about to do, Alanis quickly said "don't do it". So of course, right that moment, I decided to walk to the door, jiggle the broken doorknob, and uttered the following high-pitched complaints in quick succession for Lilandra Marie to hear.

"This is so, like, *cumbersome!*" I said in a valley girl accent. "Maybe if someone will volunteer to buy a lock that, like, snaps back automatically it would be best for, like, everyone!"

Followed by:

"I need four hands to open this lock, to turn the key, to hold my chilled taho, and to scratch my head in puzzlement."

And finally:

"If there are four locks, three mutants, two cedar trees, and twelve keys, with the variable x approaching y asymptotically, would you agree that..."

"That… is… it!" Lilandra Marie suddenly screamed. "I will open this door for you! It's so easy!" She lunged at the door, unlocked the doorknob with a flick of a finger, and shoved it open. "See? There!"

Then, with all her strength, Lilandra Marie pushed me out the door. The push was so strong I landed on my butt at the marble floor of the adjacent ophthalmology building.

"Or maybe it was just a mild-to-moderate push," Smoketh said with a forced yawn. "Or even a slight nudge of Lilandra Marie's shoulder. You were just weak."

That was exactly what I wanted her to say, and in my head, I had already justified the tactless comment I made earlier.

Lilandra Marie and I apologized to each other after that incident, but I allowed her apologies to be more profuse than mine. I mean, I had incurred a tiny gluteal hematoma. I asked her if she was okay, and she said that she was suffering from brief reactive psychosis (BRP) because of the recent mortalities in her ward service. The trigger was the faulty doorknob. And of course, my sudden transformation into a blonde girl named Chelsea sipping wine in Cabo San Lucas. Strictly speaking Lilandra Marie's outburst wouldn't fulfill the psychiatric criteria for BRP, but we had grown accustomed to misusing the term to refer to any emotional turmoil that happens among med students and trainees. Such episodes were usually characterized by bouts of weeping and complaining, and threats to abandon unfinished tasks.

Back when we were interns we saw these same signs on one of the internal medicine residents in our team, Dr. Vanessa Mae Bonaparte.

There were rumors that she wanted to quit, take the US medical licensure exams, and start a new life abroad. We were scheduled to go on rounds with our consultant the following day, and Vanessa Mae was panicking because she hadn't even started studying any of her cases. Getting scolded during the rounds just might push her over the edge, so we all had to do well.

During the consultant rounds the residents are usually asked about patient management, while the interns report basic information like history and physical examination findings. Still, we were warned that senior consultant Dr. Kara Georgina Luciana Borgia was difficult to please. With my co-interns Ditz, Myra, and Maan we asked the previous rotators for tips on how to prepare for Dr. Borgia's infamous rounds. Chepoy Marasigan, who had rotated with Dr. Borgia's ward service the previous month, said that the interns are expected to know the patient's personal and social history inside-out.

"You should leave no stone unturned. But don't worry, you'll survive," Chepoy said smugly. I told Ditz that Chepoy was probably exaggerating, that she just wanted to use the idiom "leave no stone unturned", but Ditz was not taking any chances. She assigned each intern to re-interview our service patients, with specific bullet points on the important things to ask. We shouldn't miss the basics, of course, like employment, smoking history, vices, history of travel. But Chepoy also mentioned the need to take a deep dive into the following: previous occupations, spouse's occupation, college course, specific brands of cigarettes used, the factories in the area of residence, monthly income, favorite dessert, and so on. Patient Milagros Lumbrina must have found it strange that I was asking about her dog's vaccination status, when she was simply admitted for elective coronary angiography.

I was about to go home at around 5 PM, but I saw Maan still feverishly talking to her patients. She seemed to be enjoying it. Not to be outdone, Ditz, Myra, and I went back to the patients we had already interviewed with a brand-new set of questions. The goal, apparently, was to craft an authorized biography for each patient. Come to think of it, Dr. Borgia's style of rounds wasn't really *that* unique. When we were rotating as interns in Pediatrics, I once reported to Dr. Athena Motherella Thunderella that the usual diet of my patient, a 3-year old, was composed of meat and rice. Seemingly insulted at my lack of effort, Dr. Thunderella glared at me and asked: "Yes, but does he chew the meat then swallow it? Or does he chew the meat, suck the meat juices, then spit the meat out? Or does he chew the meat, suck it, then swallow it? Or does he chew the meat, suck the meat…" If Dr. Borgia was anything like her, I would go into a BRP myself.

Day of rounds. Dr. Borgia asked Maan what patient Romulo Razon's occupation was.

"Patient has been working as a jeepney driver in Quezon City for eleven years," Maan said. Ditz and I smiled. Myra nodded her head in approval. So far, we had satisfactorily answered all of her questions, and we didn't even need to make Nanette. Our service senior, Dra. Donatella, and the junior resident, Dr. Vanessa Mae, were very pleased. We were doing great.

"So he's a driver huh," Dr. Borgia said, her right eyebrow shooting up, her lips curled in a sneer. "But do you know his daily *ruta*?"

Dr. Borgia must have expected her to get flustered, but Maan didn't make like a homicide investigative journalist all night long for nothing.

"He begins in Katipunan, passing by UP Integrated School," she said. "He then turns left to UP Diliman through the entrance near the Islamic Studies building, turns right to Apacible to pass by the Shopping Center and the old post office, then passes by Kalayaan Residence Hall along Roces Street. He then turns right to the corner of Molave ..."

After completing her virtual tour of the UP campus, with Mang Romulo parking his brown-roofed jeepney in front of Vinzon's to wait for passengers, Maan curtsied and waved to the crowd.

Everyone, including Mr. Romulo Razon himself, clapped and cheered.

The Legend of Thymes and Lochia

A FEW MONTHS BEFORE WE GRADUATED from residency my batchmates and I went into a mad scramble. We were panicking, not knowing what to write on our fellowship application forms, ruminating if we should undergo fellowship at all. Having absolutely no decision-making skills I asked my good friend Mrs. T what she was planning to do.

"Obviously, I will apply in oncology!" she beamed. In retrospect this could have been the beginning of a long con. I suspect that she must have been winking at someone behind me when she said that lie, because I had been trying to carbon copy her career and general life decisions since college.

"Things have been turning out very well ever since I tried to follow the path of your amazing career, Mrs. T," I once baby-talked in pure Single White Female, Misery, and The Talented Mr. Ripley stalker mode, "and I intend to keep on trying to be you." She snorted when I told her that I aim to follow her around until we are both senile and bedpan-requiring.

To sift through my options, and to illustrate that I have my own brain, I listed down all the available subspecialties and the reasons why I wouldn't want to get into them. Reality competition shows were big at that time, and what better way to make a crucial life decision than by the scientific process of voting something out. Pulmonology and cardiology: they still require overnight duties.

Gastroenterology: I have low tolerance for human feces. Nephrology: I never understood sodium. And so on. At the very last minute Mrs. T bailed out on me and decided to pursue rheumatology instead, successfully untethering herself from this needy, whiny friend with no originality.

My good friend Thymes Alvarez never expressed doubt that the right field for her was cardiology. She announced this decision while we were having dinner with Ardee in Kantunan, a barbecue joint along Maria Orosa Street. We knew she would be a shoo-in, being a walking repository of nice-to-know medical information. Whenever we ran out of things to talk about we only needed to mention buzz terms such as "Primary hyperaldosteronism!" or "Creutzfeldt-Jakob Disease!" and it would trigger an intellectual masturbatory soliloquy, whereupon she would quote paragraphs upon paragraphs of pure Harrison's Principles of Internal Medicine 17th Edition goodness, complete with fine print and algorithms in full colour. Thymes is one of the smartest in our class, and we've always suspected that she either has a telepathic connection with the writers of the textbook, or she has ectopic brains in her breasts.

During the applicants' interview Thymes was ready to be grilled by senior cardiology consultants, most of whom had caused fear and trembling when we were students. She introduced herself in impeccable English, not showing any signs of awkwardness or discomfort. The consultants had already read her spectacular CV— top of the class, fantastic performance during residency, well-loved by consultants and students, accolades all over. Her self-assured demeanor and her bright red lipstick exuded just enough confidence that announced that she wouldn't be intimidated. The first question was how she would describe herself. Without batting an eyelash she said, "I'm a schizoid."

This elicited rounds of raucous laughter among the panel composed mostly of macho, middle-aged men. Dr. LGH said, "We want interesting, confident people in our section, tee-hee, but we don't want people who have… an altered perception of reality!"

Thymes indulged them and explained, with no hint of condescension, the difference between schizoid and schizophrenia, not flinching despite their persistent giggles. "Schizophrenia is the condition characterized by perceptual disturbances like hallucinations and paranoia, while those with a schizoid personality tend to prefer being alone doing solitary activities," she lectured. "People with schizophrenia will need drugs like thorazine, while the schizoid…" Technically, if we drag Thymes to a psychiatrist she will not be characterized as having a true schizoid personality disorder, but she has embraced the label wholeheartedly.

Fellowship training, as we would learn later on, has a way of overhauling one's personality. From being a self-proclaimed schizoid, Thymes quickly became the life of the party. She would go on to perform in the cardiology section's numerous variety show performances. Her star-making role was as a demon warrior-*manananggal* who engaged in a sword fight while hoisted up in the air. She officially added performance artist in her novella-thick resumé, and everyone expected her to do fabulously in private practice once her PGH training was completed.

After graduating from fellowship and acing the cardiology boards, Thymes went home to Cebu and suddenly fell off the grid. Nobody could contact her. She wouldn't take any calls, and she never replied to any text messages for weeks on end, like she wanted to disappear from the face of the planet. As we would learn later on, she had been swallowed by an emotional blackhole, the kind that appears out of nowhere during an extended state of doing nothing. For months and months, she whined about how nothing had come out of her academic achievements. At times she would just stay in bed, not taking a bath for days, standing only to pee. She likened the feeling to being a bipolar patient crashing after a euphoric state. Or like a bride who had just taken off her wedding gown after a long day of being showered with attention and realizing that she is not so special after all. Or like a cat unable to pull out that plastic strip sticking out of its ass without the help of a kind stranger, because why it even ate a piece of plastic in the first place, nobody really knew. As she would admit later on, her metaphors and similes for how she was feeling were starting to get stranger and stranger.

Thymes tried to migrate into a nearby city in an attempt to establish anything that would resemble a career. She slathered on her reddest lipstick, wore her nicest blue dress, and attempted to recapture the winning confidence that made her a star during the fellowship interview years ago. Much to her chagrin, private hospitals were not tripping over themselves to hire this topnotcher cardiologist who had graduated from the premiere medical training institution in Manila. In fact, nobody seemed to care how fantastic her credentials were. It appeared that the currency for success wasn't what one knew, but who.

"*Ano?!*" she yelped as the secretary of a clinic explained that her rate as an employee would be P100 an hour. She quickly moved to another job that required her to read ECG strips. That day she earned her first paycheck—P140 for reading two ECG's. She got into a taxi, paid P200, disappeared into her P6,000 per month apartment, wolfed down a Big Mac worth P150, and started weeping like a wet diabetic foot. Finally she looked at the skies, pumped her fists, and uttered the line that I would also scream later on when I had just finished hell-owship myself: "Fuck this shit!"

While packing her bags to go back to Dalaguete, Thymes saw an online advertisement for a cardiology position in Sultan Kudarat. She only needed to email a letter of intent, and a plane ticket would be sent to her the very next day. Ardee and I warned her that this plotline sounded very pretty girl being promised a modeling job in a faraway land, only to land movie deals as an ST starlet.

"The more I should do it then!" Thymes said with finality.

She had never been to Sultan Kudarat, but as soon as the plane landed, she felt like she was home. She immediately became the queen cardiologist of a tertiary hospital and twelve secondary hospitals in the neighboring towns. She found her place, and from a simple Dr. Thymes Alvarez she had evolved to become the one, the only Sultana Kudarata.

Thymes' fantastic stint as a fellow became the stuff of legends, and over the years new applicants have tried to bring as much zest and personality to the section. One such applicant to the throne was Lochia, who was a repository of all kinds of medical knowledge himself. During his interview he was asked "Why did you choose cardiology?" Most of the applicants replied with trite but not necessarily untrue answers such as "To serve; there are no cardiologists in our province; my father died from dilated cardiomyopathy, etc". Thymes' answer to this question was: Because it's glamorous!

Lochia, attempting to forge his own legend, didn't fail to astound. "Why did you choose cardiology?" the top cardiologists of the country asked. With a straight face Lochia said, "I've been thinking about that question since last night, because I knew you were going to ask that question. But you know what, cardiology is not the question. It is... the answer."

The crowd broke into applause.

The answer didn't really make sense, but who cares.

The Telepaths In The Callroom

IN THE MIDDLE OF WOLFING DOWN shawarma for lunch I decided to quiz Lochia to assess his readiness for the upcoming specialty board exams. Residency was winding down, and we only had about a month or so to prepare for it. We all knew Lochia would be able to breeze through standard textbook-based questions, so I told him I would just mention key phrases and see if he could guess what I was thinking. Joining us were Tolits and Diana.

"Hey Lochia," I said, "Category: Infectious Diseases. Question: 8-16 hours?"

"Bacillus cereus," Lochia, Tolits, and Diana chorused nonchalantly.

"Correct!" I exclaimed, pretending to slow clap in astonishment as pure panic gripped my innards. I was hoping they would snicker and complain that it was a ridiculous "question", that there was no way they could figure out what I was thinking based on that generic tidbit, and that it wasn't even a legitimate buzz term, but they all guessed correctly that I was pertaining to the incubation period of bacillus cereus food poisoning. I could assert that Lochia, Tolits, and Diana had memorized Harrison's Principles of Internal Medicine to the point that they could quote passages on cue and come up with a brand new organized religion, but they had evolved way beyond that. Like Thymes before them, they had mutated into telepaths.

Later that day I shared this harrowing experience to our other residency batchmates, Lloydie and Mars, over late-night coffee in the callroom. I was hoping to find solace, but they decided to intensify the panic instead.

"If I don't pass the specialty boards," Lloydie said with much drama, "I will completely disappear and erase all traces of my identity from the internet!"

"If I don't pass the boards," Mars said with more drama, "I will not attend the graduation!" The residency graduation ceremonies were conveniently scheduled days after the release of the specialty board exam results, further amping up the pressure.

"If I don't pass the boards," I started, because I had to win this whining contest, "I will still attend the graduation so I can observe how people will sidestep the issue. And I will try to catch their furtive glances, and hear their carefully-worded conversations, their restrained congratulations, and sense the general discomfort at having a failure—me—around. I will enjoy being the giant elephant in the room that nobody wants to acknowledge!"

"Or so you think," Lochia said, who was apparently not asleep and had been eavesdropping the whole time. "So you think that people will tiptoe around you. For all you know the department chairman will go to the podium and announce 'Congratulations to everyone for passing the specialty boards, everyone except Will! And he attended my boards review for free, if I may add!"

I never felt more motivated.

HELLOWSHIP

Even Ducks Get Liver Cancer

"OBVIOUSLY, HEPATOCELLULAR CARCINOMA!" Doctor Caligarius announced as he raised the CT scan films of my father against the dull fluorescent light. "Poor prognosis, let's say, 6 months!" Clearly, he did not believe in beating around the bush, or maybe he was rushing to catch a plane.

"What's the cure?" I stammered. "I mean the palliative treatment, if it's not curable. Chemo?"

"Chemo won't work. Doesn't look resectable, either. Just give him all the delicious food he wants!"

In that bizarre instant I felt like I was in a studio of a poorly written comedy sketch, or an 80's TV-drama where all cancer patients had 6 months to live. Good thing I came to see the world-famous Doctor Caligarius by myself, because it was such a terrible disclosure that I did not want my father to experience. I wasn't looking to have my hand gripped in full emotional support, but I wasn't expecting to get knocked off my senses either. And that tone. That cheerful, repulsive tone. I was reminded of a high school classmate declaiming Walt Whitman's "Oh Captain, My Captain", and was told by our English teacher to stop being too darn cheerful. He was smiling all throughout the piece, even in parts where the captain is "fallen, cold, and dead".

I entered oncology training four years later, and on my first day I promised never to make my patients feel that disclosure is like a crop of hair getting stripped off by a powerful adhesive. I tried to recall moments when I felt nervous talking to someone about matters of life and death, to sort of review my track record. What immediately came to mind was my stint as a peer counselor back in high school. A guilt-ridden freshman once told me that he had masturbated six times in one day, and that he felt terrible. I was stumped, so I told him what any good Catholic would say: if you really feel bad about it, confess it to a priest and receive your penance (about five Our Father's). I must have sounded too judgmental, and a bit dismissive, as I exerted no further commiserative efforts. Looking back, I think he was just bragging.

In came the first patient. I turned on my peer counseling voice and, unable to find a box of Kleenex, brought out a roll of flattened toilet paper from my backpack. I asked him what he understood from the biopsy result, and what he might have read about it on the internet.

"It's cancer!" he said, with more enthusiasm than I had anticipated.

Well, that was easy.

To my surprise many patients didn't seem to require any formal disclosure of their cancer diagnosis at all. Perhaps the referring physician, or the metal-plated marquee that says, "Cancer Institute", already did most of the talking. It wasn't called a "Wellness Center" or an "Institute of Neoplasms and Other Euphemisms" after all. Obviously, disclosure is more than revealing the diagnosis, but putting a label on it is the most difficult step in the process. At times there were others who would fail to catch on, and this difficult situation would be exacerbated by the patients' relatives themselves. Before I could even start my spiel, some relatives would strategically stand behind the patient, glare at me, and make all sorts of gestures to restrain me from revealing the truth. Said gestures included waving, shaking their heads aggressively, wagging their fingers, all culminating in a full-on interpretative dance. And the strangest of them all given the context of the consult: doing the throat-slitting gesture with a thumb.

"It's always best to be direct," one of our mentors had advised at the start of training. "Look into the patient's eyes, don't fidget, be gentle but straightforward. And whatever happens, don't be that idiot who cries first. The last thing we want is for the patient to be consoling you." At times being upfront did seem effective, but without proper execution it made us look like snot-faced amateurs with horrific bedside manners. A sister of a terminally ill patient once threw a literal wet towel to my face when she didn't like the manner with which I said, "cervical cancer stage 4 with metastasis to the peritoneum, adrenals, lungs, and brain, and it's also causing urinary obstruction. I still have to check how chemotherapy will be adjusted in the event of hemodialysis, but don't worry, I think…"

Thwack!

When being "direct but gentle" wasn't proving to be too successful, I tried to vacillate and beat around an entire forest. Not only did my declamation piece confuse everybody, it also made me look like a total moron stammering and blinking and snickering inappropriately.

Mr. JK, who came in with test results that screamed an unequivocal stage 4 melanoma, had asked me point blank: "Cancer po ba?" And, remembering the sopping Good Morning towel to my face, I said the most annoying euphemism anybody could use in that situation: "Yes, it's cancerous". As if the extra suffix could soften the blow. He already asked, so it was the perfect opportunity to answer with conviction that yes, it is cancer, not "cancerous" as if it is almost cancer but not quite there yet. And given the extent of the disease, it is *so* there that the appropriate suffixed term is more like cancerrific. I did not want more towels hurtling towards my face for a pathetic attempt at levity, so I opted not use that term either.

We therefore resolved that nobody could do a perfect disclosure all the time, and it had taken us multiple rounds of hits and misses before we even became comfortable doing it. Disclosure is a skill. It needs practice, and everyone had their moments of being horrible and crass. I once heard a colleague tell a patient with utmost seriousness, empathy dripping in her voice: "Whether a person has cancer or not, young or old, male or female… the important thing is to die with dignity." She didn't get a towel to her face, because the irate patient stood up and left. I once told my clearly distraught patient the scintillating trivia that in China even ducks get liver cancer. I didn't really know what I was aiming for.

One of my earliest lessons in telling bad news was during internship, when the OB-Gyne resident Dr. Alice and I had to reveal to a post-operative, groggy mother that her first born had died. Mrs.

dela Cruz was still too woozy to respond with the appropriate affect, so in a way Dr. Alice got a convenient pass. She was then summoned for another surgical procedure, and she quickly instructed me to extract all the details needed for the baby's death certificate.

"You have to talk to her in layman's terms," Dr. Alice instructed. "You have to use the vernacular to make sure there's no misunderstanding. You have to translate. You have to be precise. Also, for all patients admitted in this area, you have to do the bloodwork, monitor vital signs, drop the referrals, prepare for the morning rounds, and be on the look-out for the next surgery that will require an assist."

It was my first time to fill up a death certificate. How difficult can this clerical job be, I thought.

"*Ano po ang nais ninyong ipangalan sa nasira ninyong supling?*" I asked very slowly, making sure to enunciate each word.

"*Matthew na lang,*" she said, her words slurring, eyes closed. It was not the best time to be asking too many questions, but the interns were quickly getting called for assists. I was next. If I failed to do this now Dr. Alice would yak at me as if I had misplaced a resected myoma.

"*Ano po ang pangalan ng tatay ni Matthew?*"—upon which a brilliant idea belatedly dawned on me that I should be asking the father for these details instead.

"Huuungh?" was all Mrs. dela Cruz could muster.

I repeated the question. Dread gripped me as I looked at the numerous blanks that I still had to fill-up. Nurse Menchie was already approaching with a tray of vials and syringes for blood extractions.

I went through the questions and continued to ask Mrs. dela Cruz. Luckily she was getting more cogent. She started telling stories about how she got pregnant, how the guy had abandoned her, and so on. It was her first opportunity to process the events so I decided not to rush her. Her stories also served as delaying tactic, as the next question seemed like a hard one to ask: the preferred mode of body disposal.

"*Gusto nyo bang ilibing ang katawan ni Matthew,*" I started. "*Gusto nyo bang ilibing ang katawan or...*"

What the heck is the Filipino translation for cremation?

"Huh?" she asked.

"*Gusto nyo po bang ilibing si Matthew, o kaya...*"

Kremasyon? Who uses that?

"*Yung baby ninyo, ano ang gusto ninyong gawin sa kanya? Ilibing o...*"

"*Ilibing o ano po, doc?*"

"*Ilibing o... sunugin?*"

"Come on, don't be so hard on yourself," my friend Jonah later consoled me after finding me in the students' quarters, visibly distressed and consumed with guilt. Jonah was a natural at establishing rapport with all kinds of patients, and he never seemed awkward talking to them. He would have fared much better in the simple task that I had miserably botched. If there was ever a time that I deserved to file an incident report on myself, that would have been it, for assuming that the service patients were so unlearned as to never have heard of the word "cremation", for deliberately speaking so slowly as if I was talking to a moron, for dumbing down words instead of translating, for being insensitive.

"It could have been worse," Jonah continued. "You could have said *silaban*, or maybe…"

We had a lot to learn.

Reasons to Quit

"NEXT MONTH, OR MAYBE NEXT YEAR!" Ms. Gwyneth, a med rep, would tell me every time I groveled for my stipend during fellowship, or as I preferred to call it, hell-owship. At that time we were at the mercy of well-meaning pharmaceutical companies for our monthly "allowance" since the hospital could not afford to provide government salaries for everyone—as if being given the opportunity to manage five cases of the rather rare penile squamous cell carcinoma in a year (something a private practitioner would be "lucky" to see in a lifetime) would make me impervious to hunger. As if the live chickens, live turtles, live goldfish I receive from charity patients could be passed on as rent to my landlady who was chronically livid and one promissory note away from kicking me out of my tiny hovel of a room which I had affectionately called The Coffin.

After six months of stipendlessness, my penchant for the dramatics had worsened and Gwyneth would hear all sorts of histrionics from this disgruntled, whiny fellow: Gwyneth, I've been feasting on sardines for over a week now! I've been stealing office supplies from the clinic! I ask someone with a car to slowly run over my tube of toothpaste to ensure I'm not wasting anything! This morning, our clinic secretary Cathy exclaimed that her giant pack of Nescafe 3-in-1 in the pantry has gone missing again. You know who's been pilfering it? Me! I am just so extremely poor!

Gwyneth would just sort of smile/smirk/wince. I could no longer tell if her smile was from annoyance, pity, or botox gone wrong, making her look like a surprised garoupa. She would then mumble some word salad, making sure that it had the word "follow-up" somewhere, after which she would bribe me with KFC which I would skeletonize in two minutes. If I was lucky, she would throw in a box of Krispy Kreme's too.

It was during those low, embarrassing moments of nibbling on the Kit-Kat bar impaled on the chocolate-frosted donut while watching Gwyneth tossing her hair and laughing—laughing! —that I would wonder if I had taken the right career path. When I was eight my pediatrician wrote on a piece of tissue paper the number of years it would take to finish each segment of medical training. She had encircled the total: 15 years. In my head then: that can't be right, I'm sure she's just trying to dissuade me. It couldn't possibly be, like, literally 15 years, right? To leave things to chance I took a college course that would allow for diverse career options should I change my mind, until I discovered that ninety percent of my block mates would go into medicine, and who was I to not conform.

There was a coffeeshop along Adriatico Street, which we called The Shrine Motherfucker, where I would meet my friends late at night to engage in a competition of whining. Over a tiny cup of coffee nursed for hours we would try to one-up each other on who was having a more miserable time, and gossip on which hospital personalities were the latest objects of collective revulsion. Half the time I suspected that we were all just being theatrical, that we were nothing but disgruntled adults who grew up in relative privilege, and now whimpering at the deprivation of certain comforts that we felt we deserved. It was a case of either being performative for the sake of it, or using theatrics to cope with the legitimate struggles of being in hellowship training.

One of the regulars in the Shrine, Smoketh, would bemoan the toll that prolonged training had taken on her dating life. She hadn't dated in many, many years, and she felt like she would be a shriveled prune besieged with hot flashes by the time she completes fellowship. Another regular, Frichmond, had been contemplating on packing her things to fly back to the province as a general pediatrician. Her father was sick, and she wanted to be there for him. At this point in our lives the reasons to quit had become wildly varied, and they had evolved from the puerile ones that we had when we were in med school, internship, and residency. This time, we felt like our reasons were more valid, and more elegant. Death in the family, poverty, romance—very elegant, indeed.

This would be in contrast with my reason to quit back when I was a medical clerk, which was the very definition of something that was not elegant. As a rotator in the OB Admitting Section I was assigned to get the blood pressure of all the women cramped in the cervical cancer corner aka The Garden. While doing my blood pressure rounds, we noticed a very pale patient staggering out of the bathroom, and it seemed like she was about to collapse on the floor. I immediately ran to her and caught her from behind like a hero, while everyone in The Garden gasped in panic. After she was assisted back to her bed, everyone shrieked when they saw that from the chest down, I was covered in her fresh brown feces. I ran—ran! — to my dorm covered in human shit, a la Tim Robbins from The Shawshank Redemption, bemoaning my fate and contemplating on not returning to the hospital. I didn't sign up for this, this can't be happening, this is the straw that breaks the camel's back, the final affront, the last straw. "I am going to quit," I declared. Half an hour of furious scrubbing later I was back in OBAS.

"*Pahiram ng ballpen, hindi ko mahanap ang ballpen ko,*" I begrudgingly asked Intern Ian.

"*Andun yung ballpen mo!*" Ian said, snickering as he pointed to the restroom.

On the floor of the restroom was a huge cake of turd—the motherload of the patient who had just passed out. And there it was—my ballpen, standing proudly on top of the mound, buried deeply like the US flag in Iwo Jima. No, not elegant at all.

Tales of Terror and Relief

BY THE TIME HELL-OWSHIP WAS HALFWAY THROUGH, my father's condition was turning for the worst. Five years into his liver cancer we had already tried every treatment available, and with his rapidly declining performance status I opted to give palliative chemotherapy at home. In the middle of my hospital duties he would call to boast of miniscule wins such as having enough energy to fix a broken electric fan, or having enough appetite to consume a full meal of kare-kare. It would be a short-lived win, though, as he called me up the following morning to report that gorging on bagoong had caused his legs and abdomen to bloat.

It was not a particularly fantastic morning. I woke up with abdominal pain that could very well be a second-generation liver cancer. Since fellowship started it had become a daily ritual to greet the morning with hypochondriation and despair, asking myself: I wonder what diseases I will have today? Will today be a brand new day full of fresh misery and regret? What whines will I high-pitchedly whine to the captive audience of The Shrine Motherfucker? My fellowship batchmate Alanis Cornucopia had theorized that I was merely having phantom gallbladder pain from the previous year's laparoscopic cholecystectomy. It was a totally made-up diagnosis, something meant to assuage the lingering terror that I could be harboring all sorts of nefarious tumors that were competing to kill me.

On my way to The Shrine Motherfucker that night I already had my daily melodrama involving dad's condition, my imaginary terminal illness, and my general state of penury lined-up, bulleted, and organized in my head. My friends and I only had two hours to rant to each other, and if you hem and haw with your issues you might lose the floor to explosive revelations, such as the recent rumors of gay sex in the ICU involving two closeted hospital personnel. Juicy. Now that would be a quick two hours of wild speculation.

I arrived at the coffee shop with the caucus already in progress. Through a thick haze of cigarette smoke, Smoketh was already regaling Frichmond, Cassandra, Invisigoth, and Jobert with a gripping, harrowing tale of terror. This time it was not about hospital events or weird men, but her now domestic task of getting a *kasambahay*.

In her perfect English and impeccable diction Smoketh narrated how one week ago she had secured the services of an agent who managed to provide her with two housemaids—Alice, a 59-year-old Bicolana whose husband had left her and her five kids for another woman, and Belle, a 23-year-old from Nagcarlan who needed to support seven siblings. Being a housemaid in Smoketh's enormous ancestral house was a challenging job, as one, not only had to scrub the floors or wash the dishes, she also had to clean the moat, feed the crocodiles, polish antique silverware, and make sure that everything was glistening down to the last lumiere and cogsworth.

"*Wala po ba kayong high blood, diabetes, hika, sakit sa puso, goiter, allergies, TB?*" Smoketh asked Alice and Belle.

"*Wala po!*" they jovially declared. Smoketh was relieved, as she could finally concentrate on slaving away as a dialysis fellow in PGH. The very next day, as she was driving to Manila her pregnant sister frantically called her on the phone.

"Smoketh!" frantic sister screamed. "*Bumalik ka dito! Si Alice... nag-cardiac arrest!*"

Smoketh immediately made a U-turn, imagining Alice suddenly dropping dead while scooping up wilted lilies from the moat. Maybe she had an arrhythmia, or pneumothorax from a ruptured bleb. So much for the *walang high blood- diabetes-hika-sakit sa puso-goiter-allergies-TB*! So much for her meticulous history-taking and adroit physical examination skills! She arrived at the East Avenue Medical Center and found Alice to be perfectly alive. Catatonic, but perfectly alive. From being a young doctor, she suddenly reverted back to being a med student, as she took charge of pushing the stretcher, bringing the patient to the neighboring CT scan, taking care of the laboratories, etc. Everything turned out to be normal, and when she tested for malingering by holding up Alice's hand and letting it drop on her face, she suspected that her condition was not organic. Social workers finally managed to contact the relatives, and after hours of stress they went home. Too bad Belle would have to work by herself, Smoketh thought.

The very next day, Smoketh was awoken by some panicked yelling. They were contacted by their village security guard who discovered that Belle was hiding behind the bushes near the village gate, carrying all her things!

"*Bakit nya kailangan magtago sa damuhan?*" Smoketh asked.

Apparently, Belle, after having spent a couple of days inside the mansion, had the sudden, uncontrollable urge to be with her boyfriend Ernie. This led her to hatch an elaborate plan to escape and go back to the province that same night. For Belle there was simply something there that wasn't there before: loneliness.

"This agency sucks," Smoketh muttered under her breath as she summarily fired Belle. A few seconds after muttering that statement of conviction, she rang-up the exact same agency to ask for another housemaid. She talked to this new prospect over the phone.

"*Wala po ba kayong high blood-diabetes-hika-sakit sa puso-goiter-allergies-TB?*"

"*Wala po!*"

Thyra, this new prospect, arrived at dawn. Even as Thyra was emerging from the agency's utility van, Smoketh could already see certain characteristic features: bilateral bulging eyes, huge anterior neck mass, cachexia, abdominal enlargement, some huffing and puffing, profuse sweating, all of which indicated the disease condition known as...

"Thyroid storm!" Smoketh screamed, followed by agonized howls of execration.

I took a tiny, calculated sip from my Café Americano and looked at my watch. It was already 10 pm, and eager as I was to have a few minutes for my own cathartic tales I was more eager to hear the climax of Smoketh's domestic drama.

"*So hindi nyo na sya tinanggap,* I guess," I told Smoketh.

"*Actually, dinala ko sya sa clinic at pinagawan ng X-ray, FT4, TSH, CBC, blood chem, ECG, abdominal ultrasound. Nakakuha pa nga ako ng discount eh, ang galing!*" Smoketh laughed sheepishly. "I also started her on methimazole for the hyperthyroidism. And then we accepted her."

Tepid Café Americano shot out of my nose.

Frichmond, who had been quiet the whole time, could no longer contain her infuriation. A closeted MALTA (Matapobreng Alta), Frichmond flicked back her hair, brought out her abaniko, and fanned herself furiously. "OMG Smoketh, *ano ka*, DSWD?!" For this outburst we decided right there and then that we should hand Frichmond the MALTA Of the Year Award, but the night was young, and she was just getting started. Having judged Smoketh severely, Frichmond now turned her attention to Cassandra, who had been looking quite dejected the entire night. A few nights ago Cassandra was set up by some well-meaning cousins (who should be ashamed of themselves!) on a blind date with a guy named Donnel dela Peña. We had not heard of any updates since then.

"It didn't turn out very well, did it?" Frichmond asked, her right eyebrow shooting to outer space. "Not to be a total MALTA, noh, but as soon as you said that he was asking to meet you in Jollibee Starmall I knew this would be a disaster."

Cassandra's blind date had started well enough. Donnel treated her to Jollibee, and in these times of fellowship-induced poverty a free meal is a free meal. They introduced themselves, shook each other's hands, and conducted themselves politely as strangers who go on first dates do. How are you, nice to know you, thank you for meeting me here, the traffic was horrible wasn't it? So, what do you do for a living?

"*Manggagamot ako*," Cassandra meekly said.

"*Ah talaga, yung tita ko pala may lipoma sa right shoulder, ano ba pampatunaw doon?*" Donnel asked. "*Yung isang uncle ko naman nagka-UTI. Yun naman isang pamangkin ko parang naduduling, etc.*"

Cassandra politely answered Donnel's medical queries. Those answers were essentially her last words for the next few hours, because from that point on Donnel started droning on about himself. It wasn't really a date, it was a soliloquy told in-between slurps of Jolli-Spaghetti, about his job in insurance, the motorbike he was planning to buy, and the many girlfriends he had managed to boink. The last girl he was particularly proud of, because, as he specifically pointed out, she was "an Atenean". After an hour of yakking about himself he came up for air and suddenly asked "By the way, Madam Cassandra, how old are you?"

"32," Cassandra said nonchalantly.

"*Ay! Hindi ka na magkakaanak nyan! Or pwede naman, kaso high-risk maging mongoloid,*" Donnel laughed, congratulating himself for such intelligent, knee-slapping humor. "*Ako 26 pa lang. Je je je.*"

He didn't really go je je je, but in our collective imagination he did. Cassandra then proceeded to grab a Chickenjoy drumstick and rammed it down Donnel's throat—also in our collective imagination.

The barista of The Shrine Motherfucker started turning off some of the lights and gestured that they were about to close. It was almost midnight. I finished my coffee and winced as my stomach started acting up again. I wasn't able to update them on my dad's condition, that his eyes were already turning yellow, that he was depressed, and that I'd placed him on morphine. I had a story to tell too but had decided not to insist on it this time. My friends' stories were all the therapy I needed for that night, the unintentional hilarity much more preferable over any self-indulgent sorrow.

My mother eventually persuaded me to have an abdominal CT scan done. In the past month three out of the eight oncology fellows had ordered a CT scan for themselves, because as the popular saying goes: just because you're a hypochondriac doesn't mean that you don't have a stage 4 rectal cancer with peritoneal seedings. Cassandra and Smoketh decided to accompany me, because what better way to discover that you're dying than to have friends hissing "See, we told you to get tested earlier" wrapped in beautiful, carefully worded platitudes. I had the procedure done in the then newly-constructed Qualimed—the aircon was functioning, there was that hypnotic whirring sound to remind you that you're in some high-tech device area, the gown smelled clean. I immediately regretted my blasted hypochondriac *kaartehan* as soon as the technician instructed me to drink one liter of oral contrast. The container was like the classic Magnolia Chocolait bottle of the 80's, filled with Amoxicillin or liquid Paracetamol. Or Amoxicillin plus Paracetamol, ie., *mag-asawang gamot.*

After the procedure Smoketh, Cassandra, and I rushed to the reading room to look at the CT scan plates clipped on the negatoscope.

"*May bukol ba? Meron? Meron?*" I whined.

"Well you don't seem to have liver cancer, or some stone, and your kidneys look fine," Smoketh said, running her fingers through the films, squinting her eyes to seem authoritative.

"No tumors…" Cassandra chimed in. "But look, we can see your penis on the images!"

I bade Smoketh and Cassandra goodbye, thanking them profusely for being such supportive friends. I walked back to the Cancer Institute to attend a lecture. I noted that the abdominal pain had disappeared all of a sudden. I pressed on my abdomen—no tenderness. The CT scan… cured me. I texted my mom, telling her the good news, and she had good news of her own. Dad was able to consume the sinigang he had requested, and he seemed to be in good spirits the whole day. I felt relief washing over me. I hoped it would last.

Life In The Coffin

THE COFFIN WAS A ROOM measuring 6 x 2 meters located in a boarding house meant for a family of five, but which had been sufficiently partitioned to accommodate twelve tenants at a time. Its walls, made of thin lawanit wood, were the color of a demented mustard yellow, the more to give the illusion of light, joy, and general perkiness. These walls were peppered with tiny holes, such that in the darkness, rays of pin light would aggressively trespass from the room next door. The first time I had come across these holes I immediately plugged them with modelling clay, but every now and then new holes would be discovered, making me feel like I was in an indie movie involving neighboring voyeurs who mutually spy, whisper invitations for late night sex, and eventually fall in love.

There were eight other boarding houses in the compound, which was well-known along Orosa Street for the barbecue joint situated at its entrance. At the time, the barbecue joint was fondly called Kantunan by its patrons, who were mostly medical students, hospital personnel, and employees of Robinsons Ermita. If budget was tight one could order a cup of rice, a piece of roasted hotdog, house water. Or as the name implied, a pack of instant canton. On pay days one could feast on a smorgasbord of liempo, barbecue, rice, a side dish of salted egg ensalada, and a bottle of Coke. And for those who were really in a celebratory mood, there was that most deluxe option on the menu: stuffed pusit. Regulars were quick to complain, however, that the quality of the food had deteriorated through the years. The last time I ate there their signature longganisa had degenerated into coalesced blobs of hard fat. The liempo cuts had gotten thinner. The squid was no longer as fresh, or as boisterously stuffed. Frequently the meats were served burned at the edges, such that the younger generations had unofficially changed its name from the quaint, playful Kantunan to the medically concerning Nitrates.

I had stayed in The Coffin for five years, living there all through internal medicine residency and medical oncology hell-owship. Its proximity to the mall and the hospital was its prime feature. Only two other tenants had stayed there longer. Most only rented for a few weeks or months, so almost everyone around me was, essentially, a stranger. On my way to the bathroom at 3 am, I would eye with fear and suspicion the unfamiliar shirtless men drinking coffee or walking in the dark, only to learn that they were seamen undergoing training in the nearby training centers. Initially there was an effort to be friendly, but with the rapid turnover of these tenants I decided not to bother with anything more than a polite half-smile. Very few people knew I was a doctor, and ambush consultations in the middle of flossing my teeth were few.

Occasionally I was left with no choice but to strike a conversation with people I'd hardly seen around, such as when I had to ask Mrs. Conchita Mirasol, a 58-year-old housewife from Bay, Laguna, if she could lend me a screwdriver. I had locked myself out when I went to the shower, and she was the first person I'd seen while I was shivering outside The Coffin like an idiot. This had endeared her to me, as I initially found her to be completely infuriating for always taking too long in the bathroom. If there was a queue of pails outside, for sure it was Mrs. Mirasol taking her sweet time. Eventually I learned that she had decided to rent a room in Manila for her cobalt treatment in PGH, shaming me for my annoyance. The concurrent chemotherapy and radiation treatments had been causing severe diarrhea, forcing her to always take control of the toilet.

The other transient I had gotten to know well was Mr. Raymond Tomano, one of the shirtless men I had seen snacking at 3 am. While walking to the hospital one day I saw his son, Roy, a nurse from Cebu, lighting a cigarette by a tree along Pedro Gil. His eyes were swollen from crying. Roy had just talked to their oncologist, and he was informed that the screening test results had excluded them from the clinical trial they were hoping to be qualified for. Mr. Raymond Tomano had been diagnosed with stage 4 colon cancer, and there was no way they could afford the P200,000 needed for his chemotherapy on a monthly basis. The very next day they decided to go back to Cebu to continue supportive care at home. Roy texted me a few months later that Mr. Raymond Tomano had died peacefully at home.

I labeled my room The Coffin not because a few tenants had become terminally sick or died in that boarding house, nor because of its size, but because whenever I opened my eyes in the morning there was nothing but total darkness. And it was perpetually silent, the honking of the cars and the laughter of the raucous Ermita crowd filtered by the multiple rooms flanking The Coffin. I would wake up at 12 noon after a long duty, and everything would still be pitch black, with no indication that outside, Manila was burning from the afternoon summer heat.

The Coffin was located at the far end of a long, narrow corridor. There were no windows. From the main door of the boarding house the floor slightly sloped down, terminating on the door of The Coffin. This proved to be a significant architectural finding when I was awoken one morning by the very strong smell of trash emanating from the flood that had built up while I was asleep. It had been raining since 5 am, the caretaker, Ate Lilith, said. They were not calling it a typhoon, merely a Habagat. The downward slope of the corridor floor had funneled the flood directly into my room, bringing all kinds of trash and excrement with it. However, other than extreme weather conditions, or the prospect of fire, the location of The Coffin always made me feel secure and protected. It was abominably ventilated, the air always smelled like soaked wood, but it was my private dingy fortress, a place where I could retire after a long day of hospital work. No house invasion from vagrants or robbers had ever happened during my stay. The only invasion was from cockroaches.

The worst cockroach siege in The Coffin happened in June 2008. While reading Birds of Prey one night I noticed a lowly cockroach skittering along the linoleum. I grabbed a rubber slipper and ran after it but failed to swat it when it cunningly squeezed itself into a corner. A few minutes later I saw two more cockroaches appearing on the yellow wall. I turned around and discovered another one tumbling out of a hole on the base of the wall. Before I knew it roaches were crawling and flying in my room. Clearly, they were trying to reclaim The Coffin. More cockroaches started pouring in, advancing towards me without fear or hesitation. It was a lost cause, but panicking would lead me nowhere. I walked out of there and bought a huge can of Baygon in the nearby convenience store. Sufficiently armed and hyperventilating, I sprayed the room with Baygon. I wished I could spray the mist through a burning lighter, but the last thing I needed was a criminal charge for arson.

A lone albino cockroach tried to fight off the expanding organophosphate mist by tumbling and cartwheeling around, doing all sorts of acrobatics until it could no longer withstand the poison seeping into its hideous exoskeleton. Finally, it lay on the cement floor frozen, his antennae twirling around, as if transmitting a last-minute telepathic distress signal to other mutant cockroaches for emergency atropine. I reached for the can of bug spray, raised it up in the air, and slammed it down on his albino carcass until I heard a gratifying "ckkrunch!" Before lifting the can off the cadaver, I had to make sure it was dead, so I grated the can against the floor and heard an even more gratifying "sqshshquck!"

I finished my toxicologic massacre at around 10 pm. I swept all the roaches into a dustpan and counted them. Twenty-four roaches, including the macerated King Albino. I thought I had imagined it all, but the next day when I went on duty in the intensive care unit I saw my batchmate Lilandra Marie visibly shaken, giant eyebags drooping down her cheeks. She was also renting an apartment in the same area, so I asked if her house had also been turned into Joe's Apartment the previous night. Yes, she said, she was also viciously attacked. Having recognized this shared terror, our veneers of strength and resolve crumbled down. Our post-traumatic shrieks then pierced the air, mingling with the alarms of the infusion pumps and the tired whirring of the mechanical ventilators.

Free Food

WHILE FIXING OUR CHARTS in preparation for a busy clinic day I told my fellowship batchmate Alanis Cornucopia that I wished I could menstruate. I had been getting crankier than usual, the tiniest micro-aggravation making me feel like—there's just no English equivalent for this term—"*pinagsakluban ng langit at lupa*". I wanted to believe that I was a calm person by default, but there was just something off in the past few days that I could not put my finger on. Maybe an occult brain tumor, or syzygy. For instance, while reconstituting the chemotherapy drug cisplatin, I discovered that I did not have a single piece of gauge 19 needle with me. This led to minutes of melodramatic loathing and self-flagellation. I ran across nurse stations in search of a needle, and saw senior fellow Bernadette looking a bit rattled herself. I'm sure she's anxious over something very small and negligible as well, I thought, I'm sure she's micro-aggravating too, I'm sure she's also—dare I say it—turning a mole hill into a mountain. I approached her so we could wallow together and find comfort in each other's shallowness.

"I was reconstituting the patient's vial of gemcitabine," Bernadette said, her right eyelid twitching. "And while the syringe was buried deep in the vial, I accidentally released it. The pressure threw the vial across the room, and it shattered against the wall. I'm now trying to figure out where to find an extra vial of gemcitabine worth P15,000!"

Back to wanting to have *regla*. I confessed to Alanis that I needed something to attribute the strange mood swings to, other than just being a bad, ill-tempered person. She revealed that she was, in fact, menstruating that very moment, to which she ascribed her sudden urge to purchase expensive gadgets. This, of course, was rooted in the ancient belief that some women turn into an emotional wrecking ball during their monthly period. I used to accuse female classmates of exploiting this as an excuse for all-around nastiness, but friends including Mrs. T would swear by it. When we were interns I once saw Mrs. T sitting on a tiny stool at the Emergency Room, weeping. Maybe one of her patients died, I thought. Or she had received bad news on the phone. When I asked her what the heck was up with the faucet of tears, all she could say was, "I have mens! I can't stop crying!"

"If you can menstruate, you'll be ten times whinier," Alanis said, as we watched patients starting to flock into the clinic. I hadn't eaten breakfast yet, and I happily discovered a half-consumed pack of *Boy Bawang* safely ensconced in my table drawer for just such an emergency. I grabbed a handful and stuffed them in my mouth. There was no breakfast sponsor that morning, not even an errant pack of pan de coco was on the dining table. I now regret having missed those wonderful opportunities for free breakfast, lunch, and dinner at the hospital mess hall back in internship. We would complain then, with fake, self-indulgent rebelliousness, that we could no longer tolerate eating mystery meat in brown sauce, that we could no longer eat silver fish drowning in some cloudy soup, and that party spaghetti is not breakfast food. But now, as a stipend-less fellow, I would feast on silver fish mixed in brown sauce drowning in cloudy soup! With vinegar! For breakfast!

In the cubicle across mine, my batchmate Carina was re-writing her patient's PCSO application papers. The patient, Mr. AL, already had 3 copies of the document in his possession, but he lost them all. Carina handed him the documents with a big smile. Mr. AL then gave her a pack of Red Ribbon Mamon. Soon enough, Carina's table started filling up with delectable goodies such as brownies, lanzones, and Mc Donald's pancakes. I walked to the other end of the room to enroll my patient in a clinical trial being handled by my batchmate Eric, and to my astonishment his table had been transformed into a veritable panaderia. There was a whole log of mocha roll, a box of assorted Dunkin' Donuts, variants of Tipas Hopia, and the *piéce de resistance*: a box of 12-piece *sosyal* Mary Grace cheese rolls! I was already on my seventh patient for the day and I hadn't even received so much as a tasty bread with Lady's Choice sandwich spread and Plus King Size bought from a cigarette stall along Faura! I wanted to think that I had been nice to my patients, that the lola's in particular still found me adorable, that my recent bout of male pre-menstrual syndrome was not affecting my patient management, but my sad, empty table seemed to disagree.

"Or how about, maybe they just didn't have money for anything other than bus fare and their expensive chemotherapy drugs, how about that?" Smoketh, in her infinite wisdom, would later tell me.

Back in med school and residency, when we still had money to eat in restaurants, I used to rebuke Smoketh for leaving the waiters tips. There's already a service charge, I would tell her.

"But similarly, whenever we are in the clinics, the patients don't have to give you a giant bangus or a llanera of leche flan after the consult," she argued, "but you feel ecstatic whenever they do." I started giving tips from then on, keeping in mind some of the fantastic "professional fees" I had received through my years of training—all the fruits, all the live animals, all the home-made ulam. The more memorable ones include: a miniature house made of chocolate, bottles of imported perfume testers, a bottle with rolled sheets of paper that had Biblical sayings on them, and my favorite: a half-empty box of Cowhead milk, for how it represented the patient's gratitude despite her station in life.

For now, though, a piece of *kalahi* would be very much appreciated.

Finally, the eighth patient, Mrs. FL arrived with a brown paper bag that seemed to contain something heavy, something edible. I inserted her IV line, gave the anti-emetic medications, pushed the doxorubicin, hooked the cyclophosphamide, all the while wondering what that brown paper bag resting on the bed must be. Differentials: a sandwich, donut, hopia, siopao? While still hooked to the chemo Mrs. F.L. finally told me that the paper bag was for me. I reached for it, thanked her, salivated. I turned around, resolving that I would eat first before calling the next patient.

I opened the paper bag and looked inside.

Atchara.

The Mysterious Mr. Q and
The Bright Orange Envelope of Death

I RECENTLY BEQUEATHED HELLIZA, an internal medicine resident, an orange plastic envelope containing enoxaparin syringes. It came in a box full of other medical paraphernalia donated by a foreign NGO. In true charity fellow fashion we lunged at its contents as soon as it was opened, clawing at each other for gems such as the chemotherapy drug gemcitabine. Enoxaparin is a blood thinner for use among patients with blood clots, and Helliza has been running all over the hospital looking for it. She has been in a state of severe emotional distress brought about by strange happenings that we used to refer to as S.A.T. An S.A.T is a patient's mysterious medical condition for which we, as trainees, can offer no logical explanation whatsoever. We would call our consultants, do all the available tests, present the cases in various multi-disciplinary conferences, and the correct diagnosis would still elude us. My residency batchmates and I used to scream S.A.T. in the emergency room when we could no longer figure out what was happening to a patient. If none of my batchmates ever recalls what the term S.A.T is, that's because nobody had ever used it. It is an acronym that didn't really catch on, because we always preferred to utter the full words in bloodcurdling, guttural voice: *Shet, Ano 'To!*

One such case that boggled the mind was of a 40-year-old male who was admitted in the charity ward for cough and disorientation, but most striking was the deep yellowness of his eyes and his skin that was almost orange. The internal medicine and gastrointestinal services had worked the patient up for all causes of jaundice—metabolic, infectious, malignancy, obstruction, poisoning, but nothing could tie all the symptoms in a neat bow. A few days into the admission the patient's cough worsened, he developed facial tics, his serum electrolytes plummeted, and he eventually died. Tolits, the resident-in-charge, was stumped on what to write as final diagnosis on the official records. He went around asking all his seniors and the experts on board, but nobody wanted to commit. It still puzzles us to this day, and we have resolved to unofficially label this diagnostic conundrum as "Fatal Carotenemia".

Clutching that gem of a plastic envelope containing precious enoxaparin, Helliza ran back to the wards. "Be warned," I glowered. "Whenever I used the enoxaparin from that envelope, my cancer patients died. Alanis Cornucopia used that on a breast cancer patient with pulmonary embolism, and the patient died. She passed it on to me, and I used it on my patient with spinal cord compression, and in a day or so, you guessed it, he died!" Lightning, thunder, sinister background music while I surreptitiously double-checked if the medicine was expired or a mislabeled arsenic. Of course, it could be argued that in all those instances the patients were already in terrible condition from the thromboembolic phenomena, necessitating the drug in the first place. But still, we could not discount the notion that this innocent-looking container could be the bright orange envelope... of death!

But truly there was no time for superstitious nonsense, primarily because enoxaparin is considered deluxe. A standard preparation of the innovator brand costs around eight hundred pesos per pre-filled syringe, to be used twice a day. This is usually too expensive for our charity patients, so the residents tend to use the much cheaper but more cumbersome unfractionated heparin. Helliza's patient, Mr. Q, a vagrant with no funds and no relatives, needed the medication desperately.

Mr. Q had arrived at the emergency room two weeks ago with a huge wound on his left leg. It turned out to be a severe soft tissue infection called necrotizing fasciitis, and immediate amputation was deemed necessary. As his resident-in-charge, Helliza went through all the logistical hoops and financial labyrinths, and successfully facilitated the below-the-knee amputation. In the middle of savoring this success and congratulating herself for a job well done as a doctor and a social worker Mr. Q developed tremors, seizures, and plunged into a coma. Not knowing what was happening Helliza tried to order all sorts of imaging tests for the brain, but she knew it would take a long time with the requests for funding, social service applications, and other infuriating encumbrances. Her service senior was breathing down her neck: What's happening to the patient, Helliza?

Helliza grabbed Mr. Q's chart and reviewed the course and laboratories, all the while murmuring, "*Shet, ano 'to! Shet, ano 'to!*" In desperation she rummaged through the mysterious Mr. Q's backpack, looking for any information that could help her, like a telephone number or a bottle of prescription medicines. She found two bottles of gin. The sudden cessation of alcohol intake when he was admitted had seemingly caused the chronically alcoholic Mr. Q to develop the neurologic symptoms. She referred him to toxicology and neurology services for co-management of delirium tremens brought about by alcohol withdrawal.

In the middle of congratulating herself for being a fantastic doctor, a social worker, and an amateur sleuth, she saw Mr. Q clutch his chest and develop difficulty of breathing. The diagnosis was not so puzzling this time around—the patient had developed blood clots in the other leg after weeks of being confined in bed, and these clots swam all the way to the lungs and blocked oxygenation. This caused Helliza to frantically run around looking for free blood thinners, and providentially I was ready to pass on the Bright Orange Envelope of Hope (its original name). By the time she was able to go back to Mr. Q he was already being intubated by her batchmate Mabelle. Social services were still unable to contact any relatives, so there was no one to provide any advanced directives. In the middle of intubation he developed seizures and went into cardiopulmonary arrest. Five minutes into the CPR Mr. Q was revived. Helliza hastily gave the first dose of enoxaparin.

That night Helliza called to say that The Mysterious Mr. Q had died. In the hurly-burly of things—the resuscitation, the transfer to the ICU, the service meetings to discuss the next course of action, the envelope had suddenly disappeared. She searched all over the wards, in the residents' quarters, in the nurses' station, in every nook and cranny, every crevice, but the bright orange envelope could no longer be found. She was able to use only one syringe. Her batchmate Arabella seemed fidgety the entire morning, and Helliza suspected that she had stolen it for her own patient. In the nurses' station Helliza hovered around Arabella trying to catch her with an enoxaparin, but she instead reconstituted the lowly unfractionated heparin. Helliza gave up.

"Let it be," I declared, insisting on playing the role of a disenchanted marm. "It is an orange envelope of doom that should never be found."

Which suddenly reminded me, written on the orange envelope is my name. In case anybody finds it don't return it to me, throw the cursed thing away. Throw it away! Or donate it to patients with excellent prognosis to begin with.

Capsule Quest

MARCO SILVA, ONE OF MY PATIENTS from Tarlac, had called me on the phone one morning to ask if he could come to the clinic. He was about to take this new chemotherapy drug, and he wanted me to personally teach him how to do it. It sounded like a whole lot of effort just to make me watch him pop a pill, but sure. It would be a momentous occasion after all, a celebration, as he was finally able to get sponsorship for his very expensive chemotherapy pills from a government agency. Whether the drug would work or not was not yet the issue. In the hierarchy of worries, figuring out how to finance the treatment was the primary worry. Once we got past that, then we could start focusing on other things, like the actual cancer, its complications, its potential to kill.

Marco's trek to gather enough funds for these shiny, cutting-edge medicines could be properly categorized as a quest. At 48, alone and infirm, Marco was not in the best condition to be going around Manila, sleeping on make-shift cots to keep his spot in the queue, making sure that he always looked miserable enough to be pitied. But he did not really have a choice.

After I had given him the required papers, Marco had to commute to the government office to file them himself. Said papers included a medical abstract, chemotherapy protocol, medical certificate, progress report, and chemotherapy prescription. Some screeners were harder to please than most literary or medical journal editors.

If you labelled a document as a "Clinical Abstract" instead of a "Medical Abstract" they would summarily reject it and require the patient to return all the way to the hospital to have it replaced. The requirements also kept on changing and mutating depending on the person receiving them, that at some point I had labelled each page as "Medical Certificate/Medical Abstract/Clinical Abstract/Progress Report"—underlined, bold, italicized. We suspected that some screeners only looked at the titles.

On the day of the release of the guarantee letter, Marco took a jeep through a torrid November rain along Taft Avenue. The waters were starting to rise by the time he got in, and the thought of getting infected with leptospirosis lingered in his mind. A neighbor, Mrs. delos Santos, had contracted leptospirosis a few years ago when she jumped into the flood during Milenyo. The current was taking her pig away, but she was able to lasso it with adrenaline-fueled dexterity. In her two-week stay in the ICU she had to undergo dialysis, be seen by all sorts of specialists, and be on powerful antibiotics. She died leaving behind an elderly father, two kids, and five piglets.

An accident along Padre Faura stalled the traffic for almost twenty minutes. Marco started getting fidgety, the prolonged sitting starting to feel like torture. People sneered at him like he was a total diva whenever he propped a fluffy pillow to sit on, but it stopped bothering him a long time ago. Better to be stared at rather than yelp every time the jeepney hits a hump, or worse, a pothole. Not one to shy away from piquant descriptions, Marco had described the slightest pressure on his butt as like getting penetrated in the ass with a dildo wrapped in barbed wire. Or when he was talking to someone who might not be receptive to such graphic imagery, he would say that it's like having push pins embedded in his ass. None of the sterile medical textbook descriptions of "gnawing", "stabbing", "piercing", or "lancinating" had done this particular pain any justice.

The rains started to subside, and Marco watched in horror as beggars started sticking in their arms through the thick jeepney tarp. The heat inside the cramped vehicle was making him dizzy, but the driver insisted that they keep the tarps down as it would rain again soon. Marco ignored the beggars as his chest started to ache. A month ago he had developed herpes zoster, and now that the lesions were adequately healed there was still some sort of electrical sensation shooting through his chest wall. When I first told him that he had herpes he vehemently denied having unprotected sex. I had to clarify that this kind of herpes was merely some form of reactivated chicken pox, not the STD. Not that he had any recent sexual intercourse at all, protected or unprotected, the piece of severed intestine sticking out of his belly making him feel very conscious naked.

Rectal pain, post-herpetic neuralgia, humidity, the prospect of getting turned away by the agency for the tiniest documentary technicality. Marco had even forgotten his umbrella and boots, so factor in the risk of getting attacked by leptospiral spirochetes. Had this been biblical times he felt like he would have contracted dreadful boils all over his body as well—courtesy of Satan, of course—just to complete the Job archetype.

The sweepstakes office was about to close by the time he arrived. It didn't matter, he got the sealed guarantee letter. The next step was to go to the drugstore indicated on the letter to claim the crystal shard, I mean the chemotherapy drug, but it was already getting dark. He decided to go home and save it for the following day.

Marco sat in front of me all smiles. He had his bottle of mineral water ready. I would have happily listened more intently to all the gory details of his quest, the fireballs he had to dodge, the trolls he had to outwit, and so on, but there were more patients waiting. He took out the hallowed drug from his fanny pack. I expected a box with at least twenty-eight tablets. He showed me a tiny zip lock plastic bag with one capsule inside.

"After I take this capsule, when do I have to take it again? A month?" he asked. "I would have enough time to file a new set of papers before then."

My stomach dropped. I asked for a copy of the documents I had given him just to make sure I didn't make a mistake. He let out an audible gasp as I showed him my instructions on the prescription: 1 capsule once a day for 28 days, followed by 14 days of rest, then repeat. He suddenly remembered that I explained it as such, and we both realized that it was such a long time since we last discussed the need for this treatment. The painful process just to get the blasted drug took us this long. We anxiously went through the papers and discovered that he only got approved a P10,000 grant. Each capsule was priced at P8,500, so the drugstore gave him one capsule. In a tiny zip lock bag.

Marco swallowed the pill anyway and tried to feel what P8,500 was like swimming in his stomach. Nothing special, as expected. I watched in pity as Marco sat there, disheveled, gaunt, hungry. What should have been a cause for celebration became a cause for uncertainty. I would have to give him more copies of clinical/medical abstracts, so he could once again go around submitting it to Malacañang, to the Office of the Vice President, to the provincial Kapitolyo, to PCSO, to the senators, DSWD, and so on. We had become so used to this culture of mendicancy, that Marco would have to become one of those children sticking their arms inside the jeep, on a much bigger scale. A grander scale. A quest. His weapons: a pile of documents and the willingness to fawn over the rich. The government.

I asked Marco to take his lunch first while I printed more copies of his documents. He was still smiling as he walked away, quipping that he might get better funding this time around, now that the elections were a few months away.

Cancer, Cancer, Cancer

ALANIS CORNUCOPIA WAS SUMMONED to the medical oncology office for the much-awaited release of her salary as a sub-investigator in a clinical trial. Having developed vertigo and tinnitus from my constant whining that my stipend was still "being processed" after eight months of hunger and debt, she promised to drag me to a nice restaurant as soon as she got paid. We asked senior fellow Oxali to come, but she was still in the middle of drawing a genogram on a white board during a family conference. We gestured that she should follow, because we should never miss Alanis Cornucopia's promised treat of coffee and dessert.

"I'll have a double decker cheeseburger, fries, Coke, sans rival, and coffee, Gina," I told the waitress, before perfunctorily asking Alanis Cornucopia if that's okay.

Our waitress Gina grumbled, then left.

The smell of greasy, expensive food wafted from the kitchen which, rather embarrassingly, filled my heart with so much warmth and joy. It was a nice change of pace, as I was ready to crack open a pack of instant noodles for dinner yet again. Being *patay gutom* was difficult to outgrow during training. A couple of years ago, as Smoketh and I were poised to order isaw and rice, our affluent *balikbayan* friends Abby and Len-Len swooped in and dragged us to Spirals for a dinner buffet. As we walked through the corridors of food, marveling at the steak station and the tables of international cuisine and the columns of expensive cheeses, Smoketh and I looked at each other and gushed, *"para tayong nasa Wish Ko Lang!"*

But if Alanis Cornucopia thought that she could shut me up with free food, she had another thing coming. I summarily resumed my rants, which, at this junction, had degenerated into being a tired, tolerable schtick. High-pitched rants went on as such: Alanis, I have already borrowed money from everyone in the office! I walk all the way to the grocery to buy a can of sardines instead of getting it from the nearby convenience store, just to save two pesos! Every time I go to Gloria Jeans I bring an old Gloria Jeans paper cup so that I can still mooch on free aircon and Wifi, without having to order!

After a while I ran out of colorful ways to glorify and romanticize my poverty, that I allowed Alanis Cornucopia to get a few words in. She wasn't really paying attention anyway. She already heard all those stories before and no longer had any new insights. What was left to say or do, she was already feeding me for crying out loud. She was more worried about... the waitress.

"Our waitress seems thin," Alanis Cornucopia whispered conspiratorially. "Her uniform is too big for her, like she has lost a lot of weight over a short period of time. Don't turn around!"

I turned around. Gina was pouting and mumbling as she took the other customers' orders.

"She is very thin. And pale," I concurred.

The jaw-breaking cheeseburger was too salty, but I consumed it in a few munches. I drowned it with iced coffee—of course I ordered the expensive one with a dollop of vanilla ice cream. Meanwhile, Alanis was carefully sipping her tiny Café Americano as she took furtive glances at Gina.

"Yes, she's very thin," I repeated. "Gaunt. Cachectic."

We tried changing the topic. We knew we were being morbid, but we couldn't let it go. In our messed-up heads: Gina could be harboring an occult tumor in her belly that very moment, causing emaciation and pallor! She must already be experiencing some vague abdominal discomfort—cancer pain—making her inordinately cranky! Does her job as a waitress provide good medical insurance? Does she have kids? Will she need financial support from PCSO? What is her home life like? Does she live in a ramshackle hovel with her aging parents and five kids? We likened it to how our plastic surgeon friends notice even the cigarette vendor's nose, but at least there's no terminal illness involved there.

We started feeling strangely guilty. More than the supposed "clinical findings" cooked up in two seconds amidst the laughter of college students in the background, we knew that it was general profiling that made us create that entire scenario for our good waitress. Gina's looks, demeanor, and the way she spoke must have reminded us of one of our charity patients, Maricris, an OFW recently sent home by her Arabian employer. Maricris had developed severe abdominal pain while at work, and endoscopy revealed an imposing tumor caking the stomach wall. Biopsy of the tumor was signet ring gastric adenocarcinoma. No longer a candidate for a curative surgery,

Maricris underwent intensive chemo that significantly improved her condition. Confusing Maricris with Gina was not a case of a perpetually vigilant "clinical eye", we were just being judgmental, not very different from thinking that somebody looks rich or poor. If we were endocrinologists we would probably think she has thyrotoxicosis, if we were the police we would automatically conclude that she's a junkie that should be shot dead. Gina over-starving herself to fit in a wedding dress was a more plausible explanation than any of those, but there we were thinking she needs fentanyl.

"What did I miss? Alanis are you on a diet? Why are you having black coffee while Will is having a five-course meal? Is the sans rival good?" a sweaty Oxali rattled off as she took her seat. She had just finished talking to her patient's family members, who were still undecided if they should sign advanced directives or not. We asked her if we were being mean in concluding that our waitress has cancer cachexia. She said yes, because that is literally thinking ill of your neighbor.

Gina, still in her perpetual scowl, arrived with a plate of appetizers and a huge block of lasagna. Oxali gave her a polite half-smile as she did a quick scan of her figure. With that very swift glance we caught how Oxali had judged Gina herself. We stared at her, "So?"

"*Ang sama nyo*," Oxali hissed disgustedly at us.

To take the unwanted spotlight away from Gina, Oxali started telling us about One Day, a movie that recently brought her to tears. Anne Hathaway and Jim Sturgess play Emma and Dexter who started their relationship as friends, but over the course of many years became lovers. It was a standard romantic movie with serviceable twists, but what had gotten Oxali bawling was the very tragic death of Emma.

"Cancer?!" Alanis Cornucopia and I yelped in unison. "*Hindi. Nasagasaan sya ng truck,*" Oxali said.

Not everything is about cancer, we concluded. Still, as we walked out of the restaurant, I took a quick look at Gina, concerned that a tumor cell was cartwheeling its way from her ovary all the way to her brain.

Gunk!

AFTER TAKING A CUP of strong, bitter coffee I rush to the bus stop to start another week dedicated to service, research, academia, and dread. It will be a two-hour ride to Manila, and after years of commute I have wired myself to instantly doze off and wake up at the exact moment to alight in Buendia. From there I will take a jeepney.

The jeepney rides along Taft are usually uneventful, except for that one time when I sat beside a guy who was murmuring all sorts of biblical prophecies, complete with lip smacking, nose twitching, and other facial tics. I didn't think much of it then, but when I arrived at the hospital I noticed an unfamiliar hole on my back pocket. I assumed that it was from a natural rip that my fashionable friends would find completely deplorable, but quickly realized that it was, in fact, a long, clean cut, clearly from a deliberate slash. I slid my hand through the cut, and it was so deep I was able to touch my bare ass. Apparently I was so entertained by the guy's rendition of apocalyptic brimstone and orgasming harlots to the tune of an *akting na akting* absence seizure, it never occurred to me that he was nothing but a fake prophet trying to distract me from attempted theft.

Gee whiz.

The now familiar passengers of the provincial bus slowly take their usual seats. The bus is decrepit, the kind that if you so much as adjust the aircon vent, soot will fall on your head. And let's not talk about all the mysterious, coagulated stuff caking the bright green curtains. Some people don't seem to mind these curtains, though, as they even wrap their heads with it for warmth and comfort. It is an unusually cold morning. I am not in the mood to get into the politics of surreptitiously pointing the vent towards my seatmate, so I stuff the aircon with the scrunched-up edge of the curtain. Throughout this trip the curtain will drop numerous times on my face, followed by heaps of black ash.

I place my backpack on the floor, making sure that it is properly zipped-up. The bus is a shelter to all sorts of mutated creatures with entomologic lineage dating back to 1970's Tokyo, and I don't want any surprise roaches flittering out of my bag in front of everyone at the PGH Cancer Institute in the middle of disclosure. I text my mother that the bus is about to leave. I reply to all the text messages of patients, nurses, residents. I put my sunglasses on and play Tori Amos on my iPod. I am ready to sleep.

I am jolted into wakefulness somewhere in Quirino by something crawling up inside my jeans. It crawls up, up, up, until it parks for a few seconds on my knee. I squirm and squirm and squirm. It occurs to me that the bug advancing to my thigh can only be my personal nemesis, Ze Cockroach, who has found the perfect opportunity for revenge by making me look like an idiot. I wriggle, I writhe, I try to make it roll down my leg. It proves to be a challenging task, as the cockroach seems determined to aggressively make its way to my genitalia. My seatmate is sound asleep, and there isn't enough legroom in this sub-economy cabin to allow me to do a full-on Chun Li hyakuretsukyaku lightning kick.

I am left with no choice. The cockroach is rapidly climbing regions no vermin should ever climb. So as soon as I feel its outline in the upper thigh area, I squish it with my thumbs. Yes, I bleeping squish it. I hear the glorious exoskeletal crackle, I feel its cold, gooey entrails splattering on my skin. Now that it is immobile it is only a matter of making pagpag my leg, and the carcass easily plops down on the floor. There it is, the eviscerated brown cockroach with tan stripes, dead as can be.

Under different circumstances I would have gone completely bonkers, as nothing can make me scream without regard for gentlemanly demeanor the way a lowly cockroach can. Particularly the aggressive type that flutters awkwardly, deceptively, then swoops down to its target (i.e., my head), or the indolent subtype who engages in a staring contest while its antennae move in mockery and derision. However, the situation required me to have the presence of mind, to make an intelligent judgment call. Otherwise, I would have looked like a frantic character about to have his head chainsawed longitudinally in the horror movie Saw.

The bus finally comes to a stop in Buendia. I leisurely eat breakfast at McDonald's Pedro Gil and mooch on their WiFi to receive the lavish gifts that Alanis Cornucopia has bestowed upon my Snoopy's Street Fair online game. I try to ignore the icky, gunky feel of the cockroach remnants on my thigh. It must have turned into a coagulum by now.

Patient Roberto, who is scheduled for chemotherapy this morning, sees me eating by myself. He tells some bland, politically incorrect joke which makes me give a courtesy chuckle. Or maybe it's a good joke, I am just not in the mood. I flash a huge, empty grin and wave goodbye.

I walk back to my dorm, calmly sipping my morning iced tea, listening to the Beauty and the Beast song "Belle" on my iPod, smiling and nodding good morning's to the baker, the taho vendor, the street sweeper, my land lady, the new tenant. Once in my room I quickly take off my pants, and tell myself as I marvel triumphantly at the rich entrails caking my bare thigh: now that is gunk.

A Day In The Life Of

WHEN I WAS ADMITTED into the internal medicine residency program, I enumerated in my head all the diseases that I no longer had to learn and memorize, stashing such exam committee darlings as Kawasaki disease, placenta previa, and comminuted fractures into the archives of my rapidly degenerating brain. This list became even longer come medical oncology fellowship, because for the life of me I could never keep the types of leprosy or the natural course of syphilis in my memory for more than five minutes. So, it was pretty jarring when I woke up one morning to a text message that said: "Help, I have rectal gonorrhea!"

It was an old friend from moonlighting, Dr. Tommy A, who, in life and in text messages, had a penchant for sensational entrances. I would have recommended that he immediately proceed to the STD clinic, had he not, at one point or another, also diagnosed himself with lung cancer, nasopharyngeal cancer, cutaneous T-cell lymphoma, and oropharyngeal candidiasis from HIV-AIDS, solely on the basis of his tongue not being as bright red as he wanted it to be. Back when we were working as general physicians in the ER, he would drop everything in the middle of a procedure so he could palpate his own neck in search of tumors. More than once we had caught him listening to himself with a stethoscope just in case his lungs were filling up with malignant fluid. Perhaps he had already made the rounds of all the available cancers and decided to slowly graduate into infectious diseases.

"You remember Ulysses," he went on, "the hot cousin of Gemma, the girl who wore the tacky yellow culottes during Alfred's despedida…"

I was already running a bit late, imagining the consultants' private patients tapping their feet, waiting for me to hook their chemo. But Tommy's story was proving to be, in equal parts, entrancing and irritating.

"Of course, Ulysses," I replied while combing my hair, pretending to remember. "You mean you had unprotected sex with him, and now you think his semen inside your asshole gave you an STD?"

Not beating around the bush saves time.

"Well! Let's just say it's a long story. If you have a few minutes…"

I did not. Any other day I would have relished this sizzling gay rom-com slash medical mystery gone horrifically wrong, but I could only mumble tokenistic niceties—"Uh-huh, uh-huh", "That's horrible", "No way!" Not to invalidate his anxieties, but he had been a recidivist in making google diagnosis and histrionic catastrophizing. It was an accusation that he found terrifically insulting. He claimed that he had never relied on just about any random article online, because only peer-reviewed, legitimate medical journals were permitted to feed his hypochondria. I promised him I would reply later in the afternoon, but keep 'em text messages coming, the more detailed and more graphic the better!

The frantic walk along Orosa, through the College of Medicine, and finally up the Pay Wards was rife with traps. Specifically, conversation traps. One such conversation trap was my close friend, Glecy, whom I saw storming out of the elevator. She almost saw me, but I turned around in time and pretended that I was talking on the phone. She had just completed her very early rounds, and it was customary that after such rounds she would unleash a long series of rants. These rants always started with "*Hay nako!*"

After completing the chemotherapy of the patients at the Pay Wards in record time of 45 minutes I scurried to the Cancer Institute munching on a huge turon from the canteen. Alanis Cornucopia, whose cubicle was beside mine, was drinking expensive blended coffee. I asked for a sip, and, "failing to control" the strength of my sip, slurped all the whipped cream out.

Waiting for me on my desk was Tori, a 35-year-old single mother who worked as an OFW in Dubai. She was accompanied by her mother, Mrs. Marita, who handed me a huge bilao of homemade kakanin. Tori was diagnosed to have stage 3 breast cancer and underwent breast surgery two years ago. As a former beauty queen kontesera she found scalp-ablating chemotherapy completely unacceptable, so after her surgery she flew back to Dubai to live with her Arabian boyfriend, Ahmad. It wasn't long before she started experiencing recurrent low back pains, and she decided to come back to the Philippines for a consult.

Tori greeted me with a huge smile, showcasing her perfect veneers, her apprehension betrayed only by fine finger tremors as she handed me her PET-CT scan results. Ahmad would be coming to Manila in a week, she exclaimed, as I flipped through the long imaging report. They had finally saved enough money for breast reconstruction, and Ahmad would like to accompany her in shopping around for the best plastic surgeon. She had already sold some of her jewelry and would be content with her Duty Free Pandora and Swarovski for now.

Tori's infectious enthusiasm always fascinated me. I once suspected that her theatrical expressions of excitement, her huge gestures, the feathers on her hair, her loud 80's neon shirts, were but desperate attempts to bury her despair, but that would be dismissive of the genuine feelings of happiness that even the sickest are entitled to. And she was very sick. The cancer had already spread to the bones, her entire vertebrae now riddled with perforations. Without a thoracolumbar orthosis she could, one afternoon, drop her phone, bend down to reach it, and hear a crack. The resulting fracture would then slice through the spinal cord, causing permanent paralysis. Tumors peppered the lining of her lungs, and in a few weeks tubes would be necessary to drain entrapped fluid from both sides of her chest. Millions of errant breast tissue had travelled to the liver, the cancer making sure that chemotherapy would be difficult, if not impossible, to safely deploy.

Even as I was quietly reading this series of bad news, I was already running my script in my head. I was getting ready with my facial expressions, calculated, well-rehearsed, amateurish, but never insincere. It would be difficult to hammer away at such a joyful façade.

"It doesn't look good does it," Tori said, before I could even speak my first line.

"We have the following options, Tori, first…"

"First things first, do you think I can still have sex?" she asked.

"*Diyos ko, anak!*" her mother exclaimed.

The answer to that wasn't in my script, and my stuttering had completely betrayed me. It dawned on me that Tori was, in fact, the first patient to ever ask me about sexual activity during cancer treatment. I never bothered to ask how my patients with colostomies did it. Or if they even had the libido. The hair loss, the dry skin, the missing breast, the neck tumors must have totally altered, at the very least, the patients' confidence to be seen naked. The partners, too, must have had their own internal struggles, caught between the guilt of their own sexual desires, the guilt of not wanting their sick partners, and all other configurations of guilt.

"*Pwede kaya?*" Tori asked. "And if yes, what positions are allowable? If I bend over like this would…"

I pretended that I needed to make an emergency phone call, then walked over to the cubicle of my senior fellow, Heddalish, to ask for her opinion. The extent of the bone metastases made it seem like Ahmad could snap her neck just by grabbing her face for a kiss, but I really had no idea.

"I mean they're young. And sexual satisfaction is a huge component of a patient's quality of life," Heddalish said.

"Those few minutes of wild fornication can't possibly be worth getting spine surgery," I whispered.

We asked Alanis Cornucopia to arbiter, and she went into the whole "weigh the risks and benefits of the procedure" defensive rigmarole.

"It's not gallbladder surgery," Nikki protested.

"No, it's not. It's riskier," Alanis said.

In the end we finally accepted that some sexual activity will inevitably happen anyway, so Ahmad and Tori should just avoid positions that will require her lower back to bear a lot of weight. As Heddalish said, "*huwag maging acrobatic*", which opens a whole new discussion on what acrobats can do. For more support, we decided to refer her to Palliative Care Services and Rehabilitation Medicine.

"She just can't accept it," Mrs. Marita told me when Tori was out of earshot. I started explaining that the chemotherapy should be able to improve Tori's condition, but Mrs. Marita wasn't talking about the cancer. Ahmad wouldn't be coming to the Philippines, she said, starting to tear up. He had another family in Dubai, with two kids, and he would never leave them. He had already discussed the situation to Tori, but she was in denial. There won't be any shopping around for a plastic surgeon. There won't be a homecoming honeymoon. There won't be any sex.

It was a rather strange emotional cocktail. Regret, for how advanced the cancer was. Sadness, because I knew how Tori would eventually end up. Anxiety, fear, disillusionment. And now that there wouldn't be any spine-crushing sex, guilt-laced relief.

Dusk was already setting in by the time I finished in the clinic. Provincial ambulances that had brought the patients from remote areas started to depart. The nurses were quickly filing away the charts, cognizant of the unpaid extra government hours. I scrubbed my hands and my face, hypochondriating that invisible droplets of chemotherapy drugs must have wafted to my skin, initiating mutations that would manifest ten years later. I had been tempted multiple times to rib my patients that "yes, you are now a mutant like the X-Men, but instead of the The School for the Gifted, you are in The Cancer Institute". There was no way such a lame, insensitive joke would land.

I walked to The Shrine Motherfucker to study my cases, write my papers, and look for friends who would listen to me whine about the emotional demands of hell-owship. There was no one there. Smoketh was stuck in the dialysis unit, Frichmond was on a date, Kathy was doing research. I suddenly remembered that I hadn't even read Tommy's text messages—he was probably in his room that very moment, injecting anti-gonorrhea antibiotics on himself.

"Hi, would you like some coffee? Will it be hot or cold?"

I just stared at the barista, Tin, as I tried to wrestle with the thought of separating with one hundred fifty pesos for a cup of coffee. I finally muttered, "ok give me a caramel macchiato."

"What size?" Tin asked. "Do you want to avail of the reusable tumbler? Do you have a Swirl card? Do you need the internet password? Do you have…"

"Large," I said. "I want a large caramel macchiato. Lots and lots of whip cream."

The Cancer Institute Murder Mystery Hour: Massacred At Midnight

FINE, NOT REALLY A MURDER MYSTERY, or anything of that magnitude. But I've been reading a lot of Agatha Christie recently and I find it highly enjoyable whenever Hercule Poirot screams, in David Suchet's voice, "Murder!"

The mystery I'm referring to, of course, is the sudden disappearance for more than twenty-four hours now of the Cancer Institute Interns' Logbook! That precious logbook, containing endless thrills in the form of cryptic romantic doodles, mnemonics jotted down by nerds, and most importantly, the much treasured list of doctors chosen to be burned—burned!—come the interns' *Sunog*! A search and rescue operation has commenced, and there is now a growing list of suspects.

It has become an annual tradition at the Philippine General Hospital that on April 30, the last night of internship, all the interns wield their cleavers, pump their blowtorches, and troop like an insane mob to the basketball court to hold a ceremonial castigation of those who have made their lives a living hell. The reasons for making it to the Sunog List vary. Sometimes all you need is to have a resting bitch face and wham, you are in. No one is exempt: you nasty resident who threw a lochia-soaked speculum at me... burn! You foul-mouthed surgeon... burn! You crop of entitled, lazy med students who never seem to suffer the way we had suffered in our time... burn collectively!

The Sunog nomination process goes on all year round. At any given day there is an intern going on duty at the Cancer Institute, and this intern can write down his nominee on the logbook located at the nurses' station. The list is then whittled down to ten by votes. Cases for and against someone's nomination can be raised, for those intense few who care enough. Effigies are then meticulously created, doused in gasoline, paraded in the hospital grounds in a procession, and massacred at midnight. Usually these effigies hardly bear any resemblance to the actual person, so it helps if there is a distinguishing mark like a prominent upper lip mole, or a crop of curly salt-and-pepper hair.

Back in residency a couple of my classmates had earned the distinction of being included in this list of reprobates for two consecutive years. They had grown so used to being hated on that they wanted to file a protest when they failed to make it the third time.

"What, someone's bitchier than me now?" Grizelleda, an OB-Gyne resident, laughed as she flipped back her hair, sipped her Vanilla Ice Blended Coffee, and scrolled through bathroom ideas on Pinterest. "I just hope I don't make it to that deplorable *Puri* List, either. Yuck!"

The Puri List, which aims to promote good will by heaping praises at the most amazing people in the hospital, had been created long ago to counterbalance the hostile nature of the Sunog. Somebody must have come up with it primarily as a safeguard, to ensure the tradition's continued existence. But other than the amazing people who make it to the list, nobody really gives a crap about it. Nobody thinks it's cool. There is no cash prize to be won, and it is not something that can pad a resumé.

We have been wondering how the list might shape up now that the logbook is still missing-in-action. I imagine that I might be considered as a suspect, but I have no motive because I am not on the Sunog list. I know, because I checked whenever the interns were not looking. And I am not on the list not because I'm totally adorable, but because nobody knows who we are. For the most part we, the fellows, are just expressionless, nameless zombies lugging around chemo meds, an ultrasound machine, or a bone marrow aspiration set, with only one thing on our minds: is there free food in the office?

On our last day of internship, many years ago, my friends and I were unsure if attending the Sunog would be worth the trouble. We felt that it might be more fun to have our own little celebration away from this tradition of vindictiveness and misplaced hatred. We sufficiently convinced ourselves that we were mature, that we were above it, but in truth we were just lazy and not in the mood to socialize. That night Thymes, Hippura, and Ardee arrived at the boarding house I was sharing with Joey, carrying bottles of alcohol. It was the end of the world, the end of this world, and it should be bookmarked with alcoholic stupor.

Even as Thymes was singing and I was laughing and Ardee was fixing drinks, we noticed that there was tension brewing between Joey and Hippura. They weren't talking to each other, but we would sometimes catch them exchanging glances that were full of vitriol admixed with lust. They went to the garden to talk, but soon enough they were screaming at each other. We all came up with a solution to avoid the awkwardness of this lovers' quarrel: by escaping and going to the Sunog.

Also, someone texted that there was so much food, including an enormous lechon.

We staggered to the basketball court at around 9 pm. The party was already in full swing, and by full swing I mean most everyone had guzzled enough alcohol to be sufficiently uninhibited. I feasted on the carcass, lard, and drippings of the celebratory lechon, then joined everyone in temporarily succumbing to being emo. Instead of inciting rage towards the villains-of-the-year, people started crying, hugging each other, and taking endless photos with their Canon Powershots. Someone yelled, "*Ano to, recollection?*" At one point our friend Caloy got so pissed off at the incense-burning lovefest that he ripped his shirt off in fury. He then single-handedly lifted the transcription box which used to carry all of our photocopied readings and threw it at the fire. We had become too preoccupied with the sentimentality and alcoholism that we failed to burn any effigy. We had prepared to burn a certain laboratory personnel who made some of the logistics of submitting blood tests difficult, but we thought it was too petty, even for our very low standards.

After the ceremonies my friends and I decided to do some contemplative melodrama by walking along Malate. The night parties along Orosa and Nakpil Street were getting less frequent that year, the midweek quiet now conducive only to subtle invitations for commercial sex, or in our case, malignant reminiscences of the past five years. Throughout the walk Hippura and Joey were still pouting and giving each other the cold-shoulder. For years these two had vehemently denied that there was anything romantic going on between them, and tonight seemed to be the last time that they could profess their feelings for each other.

Still in a drunken haze, Joey decided to walk ahead of us. By the time we reached Roxas Boulevard he had disappeared into the night. Hippura seemed unaffected, making vapid jokes and laughing at herself the whole night. We insisted that Joey could be exsanguinating right now from an icepick to the abdomen, but she couldn't be bothered. "I don't care!" she exclaimed between bouts of forced laughter. Looking back, she must have been weeping inside, crushed that Joey was not holding her hand on our last night as medical interns. We would find out the next morning that Joey had lain on the cement pavement along Manila Bay all by himself, marinating on his feelings for Hippura, as he waited for the sun to bathe him in clarity. Hippura and Joey would both get into the same pediatric residency program the following year. Seven years later they were married.

Somewhere else in Manila, Smoketh and Frichmond were having more drinks with their sorority sisters. Others were signing out of their final hospital duties. Caloy was cleaning the remains of the bonfire. At this point in our lives, we were all afraid and thrilled for what the future would bring, unaware just yet of the crap that delayed adulthood would unleash.

Pinna Melanoma et Lymphoma

MY FATHER'S LATEST ABDOMINAL CT SCAN did not look too good, but we opted to try one more TACE (transarterial chemoembolization) anyway. The interventional radiologist needed to do the procedure in a private hospital in Ortigas, and I was kind of excited to be a bantay in a hospital where the hallways were devoid of loitering kitties, the aircon was on full blast, and the patients were partners. I woke up that morning ready to submit a leave form in the medical oncology office, when I noted that my right ear lobe was bright red and swollen.

Maybe something gnawed at it while I was asleep, I thought, as I inspected it in the mirror. My room, aka The Coffin, had been known to shelter all sorts of vermin. Hopefully it wasn't a rat, or I might get critically ill from leptospirosis, leaving my mom all alone to look after dad. I stretched my ear up—if I stretched it way up, the mass didn't look so big. I kept on toying with it until the swelling worsened, and in my mind, it was only a matter of time before it grew as big as a golf ball. I saw my friend Jamie who was buying chilled taho in the Cooperative sari-sari store, and she yelped when she saw my glowing, bright red pinna. She theorized that it was a disgusting ear zit.

"*Uminom ka ng antibiotics*," she said. I had not been seeing a lot of Jamie since the beginning of fellowship, except during conferences where we would discuss our common patients. She was training to become a gastroenterologist, so we had many colon and liver cancer patients together. For someone whom I hadn't been seeing that often I found her concerned admonishment to be very caring, very sweet, very...

"Cloxacillin," she said. "Make sure you take it. *Magpagaling ka. Hindi mo ako pwedeng iwan sa Medical Audit next week dahil dyan!*"

But if it were a zit, it probably wasn't just one zit, but ten coalescent zits, I whined. Smoketh theorized that it was an insect bite with hospital-acquired Pseudomonas infection. Probably. Ardee thought that it looked like a sebaceous cyst worsened by chronic manipulation. Perhaps. All sound, perfectly valid theories, except that I knew for a fact what it really was: melanoma. I mean, just because I had recently seen a handful of melanoma patients didn't make it not a melanoma, right? Right? Hence, in true PGH internal medicine fashion this was my final diagnosis for myself: Melanoma vs Arthropod Bite rule out Acne Vulgaris with Superimposed Bacterial Infection, Acute on Top of Chronic. Plan: A multi-disciplinary conference involving five subspecialties for coordinated management. Had I been hanging out with infectious disease specialists at that time I would have included leprosy, Kaposi's sarcoma, or cutaneous TB in my laundry list of differentials, further pushing my hypochondria to new, exciting, and totally insane heights.

Upon Jamie's recommendation I bought a box of the cheapest cloxacillin in Farmacia Fatima. No improvement at all after a week. The mass was now bigger, firmer, warmer. I would be talking to my father's doctors, or riding the elevator, or seeing patients at the Cancer Institute, and my ear would get stared at. The stares of disgust I could handle, as long as they were outright stares. Except, while I was talking to a fellow or a resident, they would talk and laugh and nod as if nothing was the matter, but I would catch them taking the most furtive glance at my pinna melanoma! If you have something to say, you better say it to my face, I thought, but really, if you have something to say, don't go all polite and stealthy and just say it to my face, y'all!

Like Smoketh did: Stop touching your pinna melanoma!

Or Katrina: Sir Will I hope you don't mind, *kadiri na yang taenga mo!*

Or my father's doctor, Dr. Janus: Oh my that looks terrible!

Although, sometimes we don't really know what we want, do we, because I'm sure if the furtive people started talking about it to my face as I had demanded, I would get all defensive and retort, "Well you don't look so perfect yourself!"

Pant

In pure, frenzied irrationality I decided as a non-surgeon to incise the damn thing by myself, and out poured/spurted/egressed gallons and gallons of pus. I cried in absolute pain as the gallons and gallons of pus crept down the side of my neck and into my shirt and down on the floor.

With all that pus I started thinking, maybe this isn't melanoma, maybe it's something more hideous, like a lowly abscess. Fine, maybe I was wrong after all. My ear, however, did not go back to its normal size after my act of self-mutilation. There was still some residual mass there, something dormant, something just waiting to explode or metastasize or turn into an alien lifeform. And true enough, as soon as I experienced some stressor—like hunger, general poverty, and my dad's hospital bills—the mass grew back!

"I think it's lymphoma," I told Frichmond and Smoketh while we were eating maki. I had been whining about it for hours on end through the snack in Tokyo Tokyo, through the kiddie play we watched, through the dinner in Aveneto, through the coffee break in UCC. Frichmond would no longer hear another word about it. "*Ipaopera mo na yan kay kuya*," she said. Frichmond's brother is a plastic surgeon.

"*Gaano na yan talaga katagal?*" Frichmond's brother asked. "*Matagal na po,*" I replied, like a true patient.

Operation day finally came and I walked into the plastic surgery clinic in Manila Doctors. All my friends were busy with things that were apparently more important than their friend's ear cancer, so I couldn't get anybody to hold my hand and endure my neediness. I was the classic charity patient with no bantay, so if I suddenly died on the table there would be no one to make decisions for me, and everyone in the clinic would get totally inconvenienced. Social service would need to come in, and a frantic search for contacts would be conducted.

With a true charity hospital mindset I had imagined that as I walked into the clinic I would be told, "*tumungo ka na*", upon which a circular cut-out would be made on the wrapping paper of the sterile gloves, which would serve as the sterile drape. It was henceforth surprising that the nurse asked me to change into a gown, and I was led into a fantastic out-patient operating theater. I gawked at all the shiny things inside and murmured, "wow, hi-tech!" As I lay prone on the operating table (which smelled great) a sphygmomanometer was wrapped around my arm and a pulse oximeter was clamped on my finger. Layers upon layers of brand new sterile sheets were placed on top of me until they covered my entire body. My right ear was cut, the mass excised, and cauterized painlessly. Come to think of it, I found the experience quite pleasurable, so much so that I might eventually cross over from hypochondriasis to Munchausen's Syndrome.

After the surgery Frichmond's brother declared that it was, indeed, an ordinary sebaceous cyst with superimposed bacterial infection. Or in layman's term, *sebo with nana*. As he was reiterating the steps on how to reduce the scarring and such I had to ask, wide-eyed, and in panic:

"*Sebo lang talaga? Wala talagang solid areas? Hindi kailangang ipa-biopsy? Walang solid areas? Any solid areas?*"

There were no solid areas.

Malate Noir:
Deluxe Convenience Store Confections

IT WAS A DEEP, DREAMLESS SLEEP, but I woke up with a start at around 8 p.m., my head throbbing like it would burst. I was extremely parched, sweat pooling on my philtrum, my shirt completely drenched. It was the summer of 2012, and my ancient electric fan had decided to conk out at the most inopportune time. I had finished rounds on my charity patients at around 4 p.m., and told myself that before getting something for dinner I would take a quick nap inside The Coffin.

I had fallen asleep with my white coat on, so my bed must be festering with drug-resistant pseudomonas by now. I should be hungry, but I had no desire to eat. Or maybe I'd just gotten sick of the overly-burnt meats served in the barbecue joint next door. I imagined carcinogenic charcoal now coating the lining of my stomach, infiltrating the mucosa, waiting for secondary insults to complete the mutation process. I had to get some air. And some painkillers for this headache. The faceless, shirtless seamen smoking in the veranda all waved "hi" as I passed them by. I ran out of the boarding house, my steps accompanied by the jingling of keys and the clacking of other paraphernalia hanging from my belt.

The street was dark, its usual denizens now crawling into its crevices to start a weekend of sin. A single nod, a half-smile, flashed to a stranger through a thick haze of smoke, might get you the cravings of your flesh. Or a stab wound to the abdomen.

I went to the nearest 7-11 and realized that what I really wanted was not rice, not paracetamol, nor morphine, but beer. I wasn't really into alcohol, but for this particular night drinking one can of beer sounded perfect. It was a Friday night. I deserved it.

I opened the store fridge, and as soon as I touched the beer I felt an overwhelming sense of friendlessness, the wave of melancholia rushing to my face along with the cold blast of air. I could probably text someone to accompany me, but at that point many of my friends had already graduated, or they were living too far away from Malate. The beer would just highlight my solitude. I decided on an ice cream bar instead.

And with a couple of licks I instantly snapped out of my melodrama. Now ordinarily I wouldn't spend on something as frivolous as an overpriced bar of vanilla ice cream dipped in rich Belgian chocolate, but the previous night I had accompanied a consultant in a French restaurant in Makati for a clinical trial meeting. Towards the end of the meeting the distinguished Mr. Timothy Simon Lee, the Singaporean sponsor, asked everyone if we wanted dessert. "Soufflé?" he suggested. I wanted to raise my hand and say, "Soufflé! I want a soufflé! I saw it on Top Chef and it looked delicious! I want one!" To my annoyance the most senior consultant said he would only have black coffee with muscovado sugar, thank you very much. Naturally, everyone around the table just asked for coffee as well. I didn't want to look like this young, petulant trainee speaking out of turn and asking for something fancy, so I relented and whispered "coffee, just coffee for me, too". Looking back, the other doctors in the room must have also wanted something more, like an avocado ricotta cheesecake topped with almonds. Well I would have wanted cheesecake too but you didn't speak up did you? None of us did!

"Do you have a ride back to your boarding house?" our consultant Dr. GC asked me after the meeting. I told him I'm taking a jeep. "No, no, no it's late. You take a cab." He then handed me one thousand pesos, at which point I imagined a church choir singing songs of praise and exultation as the heavens opened up and doves flew all around. "Thank you, sir, thank you," I said, stashing the unexpected treasure in my pocket.

Of course I still took the jeep. I could use that money as allowance for two weeks. As soon as I reached Orosa I thought, you know what, you have one thousand pesos in your pocket, you haven't had real dessert because you were too meek, you deserve something nice! I went to bed that night thinking of all the goodies I would buy for myself the next day, leading to tonight's belated treat of deluxe convenience store confection.

As I was twirling the ice cream bar in my mouth and checking out the other convenience store items, I noticed two men staring at my groin.

"*Bakit kayo nakatingin sakin?*" I asked. I started to wonder if the ravenous, masterful way I was sucking at the ice cream bar had given total strangers the wrong impression. It was a Friday night in Malate, anything could be misinterpreted as an invitation for sex.

The men pointed at the nail cutter dangling from the keychain on my belt.

Since high school I'd always carried a nail cutter with me, and I always found it to be totally uncool. The skin around my fingernails had the tendency to peel and bleed, and my mom insisted that I had developed this accursed condition because I once clipped my fingernails on a Good Friday.

"Carrying a nail cutter with you at all times is no big deal," my friend Ditz once assured me. "What's uncool and disgusting is that it's hanging from your carabiner with a bunch of keys, in full view of the public, and exposed to hospital microorganisms!"

The men kept staring at my nail cutter. How dare you judge me, I thought. If you only knew how I had settled for a pair of art scissors to cut off my bleeding cuticles when I was in elementary. How dare you judge me, I bet you cut your nails in public, like in a food court, with nail clippings flying all over. I know I'm a walking poverty porn, but it doesn't give you the right to demean, to belittle, to abase, to abash…

"*Pwede ba naming hiramin and nail cutter mo*," one of guys finally said. "*Gagamitin lang namin pambukas ng lata ng sterilized milk.*" He then raised the can of milk and playfully shook it to illustrate.

I suddenly wished Ditz was there with me so I could tell her: Now that, Ditz, is unequivocally uncool and disgusting.

THE
BUTTERFLIES
WE SHOULD
HAVE
MURDERED

Accident at The Penthouse

IT TOOK ME SEVEN HOURS, but I finally snatched a room for my dad. For years I had dreaded the prospect of having to admit him, not because of the expenses or the risk of nosocomial Stenotrophomonas infection, but because of the trials and torment that I would have to endure just to get in. Despite being a trainee in this hospital for almost 12 years now (counting med school), I did not really like the feeling of having to pull strings, or in this case, metal roller chains. Not that trying to do so would amount to anything—as a meek, lowly employee I was of the extremely low-profile variety. Besides, nobody really wants to be that hospital personnel who traipses into the wards and demands special treatment for the brother of his cousin's wife. Over the years this acute sense of entitlement exhibited by some employees and their "extensions" would come to be known as the dreaded condition associated with throbbing headaches and hysteria called Malignant Extensionitis Suppurativa.

Early that morning I dutifully lined up at the Pay Admitting Section. My father had been re-admitted so many times that I already had in my possession a mini collection of hospital memorabilia (cups, pillows, toothbrush) which aimed to compete with my action figures for space. Years after my father's death we would still be drinking cheap beer from those plastic graduated cups, not out of cathexis or misplaced nostalgia, but out of concern for the environment.

While jostling for a room for one of her patients Smoketh, a nephrology fellow, saw me sitting dejectedly among all the infuriated bantays. I had been maintaining a fair amount of zen by listening to comic book review podcasts on my iPod Touch, but I was quickly running out of episodes. Smoketh learned that my very weak and jaundiced father had been waiting in the parking lot for over six hours now, and she would have none of it. I explained the situation and declared that it is wrong to use connections, that social justice demands that all of us should be on equal footing in terms of efficiency of services, that the very essence, the very concept, the very nature of…

"*Uuuy, ganito. Favor sana,*" I heard Smoketh groveling on the phone. After a quick succession of niceties, forced ha-ha-ha's, and a triumphant "perfect!" Smoketh ended the call and gaily announced, "Room 542! Call your dad!"

Throughout med school, residency, and fellowship Smoketh had mastered the use of the rather cloying "*uuuy*" to preface a long, whiny declaration of need, ie., "*Uuuy baka pwede na natin syang bigyan ng bed sa ICU!*" to a nurse supervisor, or "*Uuuy pakisabi naman sa surgery tingnan na yung patient sa Ward 1!*" to an intern, or "*Uuuy baka pwedeng padagdagan ng crushed granola*" to the guy selling frozen yoghurt. In a hospital system where each trainee is pulled in many directions and attention is a commodity, any method to divert favors your way has become fair game. Such methods include batting your eyelashes and pouting your lips for those who can do so without looking like a duck, or reminding people of the favors you had done for them ages ago with a sprinkle of resentment and passive-aggressiveness. For example: "*Di ba, tiningnan ko yung patient mo dati* without requiring a formal referral letter. *Di ba!*"

We stayed in room 542 for almost a week this time, my father's edema from impending liver failure getting more resistant to medical management. His creatinine was also starting to climb, the threat of a grave complication called hepatorenal syndrome hovering over his head. Smoketh asked who among our nephrologists I would prefer, and all I could say was, "*Kahit sino basta yung hindi mahilig mag-order ng blood tests!*". I could only afford so much diagnostics on a hellow's salary, and the hospital expenses would only keep on piling up. As a welcome plot twist, my mother happily revealed that she had secured a five-thousand-peso guarantee letter from our governor, so I ran to the cashier to have it processed.

On the way back I heard someone hissing at me. I turned around and saw that it was a shady-looking guy hiding behind the ATM machine. I asked him what he wanted. He handed me a flyer that said: Hiring: Call Center Agents.

I found this to be quite astonishing. First, because I never knew that all this time there were job opportunities hiding inside the hospital, and second because I was curious how despondent I must have looked for a headhunter to correctly identify me as someone unhappy with my job. The moment seemed aptly providential. This made me reflect on the alternative careers I had passed up on through the years just so I could continue the pursuit of being a cancer specialist. Even as I was slurping viscous, sour dinuguan from COOP I was ruminating on the things that could have been, the alternate paths I could have taken, the diverging timelines I could have traversed, the flapping butterflies I could have murdered, anything that could have led to a less aggravating now.

Frankly, a brand new career didn't sound so bad at that point, and it didn't seem too late to make a U-turn. Many of my classmates had abandoned med school, and became successful in their respective fields. Some who finished med school didn't go into residency and became pioneers in research, pharmaceuticals, the academe, and online cooking videos.

Take for example, my med school classmate Marvin Montelibano. The last I'd seen of him was in Glorietta years ago, weeks before the Physician Licensure Examination. He lamented that he had been experiencing some financial problems and had not even started reviewing for the upcoming boards. We lost contact, and before I knew it he had transformed himself into a business mogul, now owning a huge empire of spas. Maybe I could have taken a path like his, except I didn't have any entrepreneurial skills, business acumen, or a winning personality. All I had was the ability to mope and unleash a hypersonic whine that could drive dogs insane and penetrate the time-space continuum.

When asked about alternative careers Smoketh would always say that she would probably be a musician or a teacher. Recently, though, she was presented with something completely different.

One morning while leisurely having coffee her dad, Mr. Yap, barked: "Get dressed! I had enrolled you in a modeling class."

Smoketh aspirated some rice and almost choked on some Vienna sausage.

"Kakkk.... Kaaak....Kaakkk?!"

Being at the tail-end of her fellowship training Smoketh had been trying to expand her horizons by getting into non-medical endeavors: the Rotary Club, yoga class, book clubs, international conferences, local choirs, and other exploratory avenues for meeting potential mates. Mr. Yap didn't think she was busy enough, and he had taken it upon himself to look for more opportunities that would allow her to achieve the ultimate goal: self-actualization. It was to his credit, then, that he had thought of Smoketh's potential as a fashion model.

"But..." Smoketh started to protest. In her head: Why the hell will I go to a modeling class? Why will I get up at the break of dawn, on a Sunday, just to meet people who will teach me how to glam up? Why can't I just have the tuition fee worth, what, ten thousand pesos, so I can buy clothes and make-up in SM? Why should I...

"I've already enrolled you for fifty thousand pesos, Smoketh! Get dressed and get in the car!"

In the class were mostly nubile teenyboppers, all of them earnestly trying to become professional models. Smoketh easily made friends with a couple of women who were more her age. There was Dra. Serafina, a dentist who was a recent separada, and Zara her kumare who, using her online investigative skills, had discovered the cheating ways of Serafina's husband. Smoketh initially felt guilty for having pried into this stranger's private life, but realized later on that she didn't really pry, the two women had laid everything out with glee within the first five minutes of the conversation. To make-up for this perceived transgression, Smoketh complimented Dra. Serafina on the tautness of her face.

"It's like I'm perpetually inside a wind tunnel, *noh. Mura lang yan*," Dra. Serafina laughed.

The students were introduced to Mr. Allan Dulcinea, a middle-aged guy who would be directing the entire modelling bootcamp. Allan ordered Smoketh to walk and strut and toss her hair while electronic dance music was playing in the background. She started off mumbling with resentment—she could be napping right now, or reading Ethiopian poetry. Or trying to understand the physiology of sodium and water—that would be preferable to this. These ungrateful thoughts, however, quickly vanished when she realized that she had a natural skill in doing a quick pivot without losing her balance. Allan also praised her posture, her rhythm, her natural bounce, and this propped up her confidence even more.

Serafina and Zara didn't get such kind words from *the* Mr. Allan Dulcinea, did they, Smoketh snickered.

And just when Smoketh assumed this was all for fun, Allan made an announcement.

"Ladies, for your final exam, we are going to hold a fashion show… in the lobby of Trinoma!"

Since then Smoketh had been attending the training once a week, taking the lessons to heart more than she would admit. Her face would be assaulted with cakes upon cakes of make-up, she would wear stilettos, and pose in strange post-modern contortions. She was really starting to enjoy herself, but she vowed never to show those photos to anyone. A few days ago, while waiting for her date in Kopi Roti Katipunan, Smoketh frantically gave me a call. I was dad's companion in the hospital that day, and was getting bored out of my wits.

"Will!" she yelled. "Allan said he posted one of my modeling pictures online and tagged me! I don't have internet right now! Here's my password, erase it erase it *erase it*! Wait, how do I look in that photo?"

I quickly erased the photo as instructed... after saving it in my hard drive! The said photo, taken from a bird's eye view, shows Smoketh lying on a marble floor with her long hair spread out, her right leg folded under her left leg, her neck hyperextended. She was totally dolled-up, but she looked a bit stoned, her eyes all glassy. Sort of like a washed-up model who had snorted too much crystal meth, gotten woozy, and plummeted down the pavement from her penthouse balcony.

Dun-dun.

"*Para kang nahulog from the top floor at nagka Locked-in Syndrome,*" I told her. "*Pero yung ibang pictures maganda!*"

Smoketh failed to parlay her short modeling stint into a career, but her confidence had shot up to astronomic levels. Her posture had never been better, and in just a few weeks she had lost eight pounds with no evidence of malignancy. Clearly, it was a fantastic step in the right direction. She also became an unwilling confidante among the younger aspirants, who were very comfortable telling her their romantic problems, financial woes, and medical concerns. While buying snacks in Mini-Stop, co-aspirant Rozabelle asked Ate Smoketh what could be causing her palpitations. Having just conducted a lecture on palpitations weeks ago, Smoketh confidently said that the most common cause of palpitations among young women is psychogenic.

"*Bakit, hija, may problema ka bang iniisip ngayon?*"

In the cashier area of the convenience store Rozabelle hugged Smoketh.

"*Nag-break na kami ni Neil, yung boyfriend ko.*" Rozabelle said.

Smoketh was taken aback, not expecting a hugging denouement inside the store. She rolled her eyes a bit, and just hoped that Rozabelle wouldn't full-on cry.

Rozabelle full-on cried.

"There, there, Rozabelle," Smoketh said while patting Rozabelle's head. "There, there."

Yellow

MR. JOEY SANTOS HAD LONG BEEN CONSIDERED a "high profile" patient in the private wards, not because of his wealth or good looks, but because he had been extraordinarily compliant with all of his treatments in the past six years. Many in the hospital staff had become friends with him, and he felt, with much regret, that the hospital was his second home. When he was 28 years old he was diagnosed with early stage colon cancer, and since then his battle with the disease had never really let up. The cancer recurred, responded to treatment, returned with a vengeance, responded yet again to a new cocktail of chemotherapy, and so on. At this point he had already undergone two major surgeries, three varieties of intense chemotherapy regimens, microwave ablation, and a clinical trial. After the second recurrence he stopped hosting a thanksgiving party or writing a celebratory essay on social media. He accepted that he would have to deal with this disease all his life, and that those misleading victories should no longer give him false hope.

Joey used to be an assistant professor in a university, but the disease had insidiously taken over his schedule. Colon cancer became his primary career. Consults had to be scheduled separately with his army of physicians: gastroenterologist, oncologist, surgeon, pain specialist, palliative care specialist, interventional radiologist, etc. Stewardship was wanting: one specialist wasn't available on this day, the other one was available but had to rush to a procedure, a reliever was available but old paper charts were missing, and so on. Imaging and blood tests became more frequent and unnecessarily repeated because nobody knew that they had already been done recently. It would have been a simple job for a wedding coordinator, and Joey's sister, armed with an accordion folder and Microsoft Excel, was up to the task. His elderly parents took turns queueing in various government agencies, their frailty an asset in the art of begging. His boyfriend Mike was his constant companion and primary caregiver. The disease had evolved into a full-time job, a production number. Not that we were any less devoted to the other patients, but each new fellow taking on Joey's case would feel especially pressured to not botch anything.

I went inside Joey's room carrying IV bottles and other paraphernalia needed for preparing his medications. His bed was empty, and I smelled the characteristic stench of cigarette smoke that I had already come to associate with him. The bathroom door was half-open, and inside, Joey and Mike were smoking, taking turns to blow the smoke through the tiny bathroom window. They had with them a handheld electric fan to hasten the egress of smoke. "Sorry, sorry," Mike sheepishly giggled, as he reached for the can of lavender air freshener that they would always bring for such a situation. I rotely tsk-tsked this time, having already given them a sanctimonious lecture on smoking, expensive teeth-whitening procedures, and exploding oxygen tanks the last four times I caught them. I proceeded to instruct Joey to take a seat on the bed so I could do a physical.

It was very apparent that Joey had lost so much weight since the last time I'd seen him. He was very weak looking, his walk from the bathroom to the bed like an excruciating pilgrim. The skin under his eyes was starting to sag, his temples were receding, his once muscular arms now emaciated. He had been involved in all kinds of sports since his youth, but he hardly touched a basketball or a badminton racquet in the past few months.

"Can you face the window," I requested.

Under the natural morning sunlight, the yellowness of his eyes was more glaring, as though the sclerae themselves had absorbed and trapped the brightness of the sun. "The jaundice became obvious two weeks ago," Mike, a registered nurse, reported. It was also around the same time when he started losing much of his appetite. Among all the symptoms of cancer the one that I dread the most is anorexia, as it frequently augurs speedy deterioration. It also triggers fatigue among the caregivers, as the patient usually requests all kinds of food in an attempt to find something palatable, only to turn it away after just one bite. "*Nailuto ko na lahat ng pwedeng lutuin!*" a caregiver usually remarks in exasperation. It is part of the cancer armamentarium, I sometimes bother to explain, the tumor releasing chemicals that trick the patient not only into disliking food, but into getting appalled by it. Not that it amounts to anything more than a nice-to-know trivia.

With the multiple recurrences Joey's cancer had acquired enough mutations to cunningly subvert treatment. This was not lost on him. In the past few days fatigue had been horrible and he would opt to stay in bed most of time. The only things making him happy were having coffee and smoking with Mike. This was in contrast to how he was during the first year of his treatment, when he would do chemo, go to work the following day, and party that night.

I lifted Joey's shirt. His distended belly was covered by purplish veins branching and re-branching into ever-thinning vessels, the skin straining from the pressure underneath. I did not need to touch it to know that the abdominal pain had worsened, that morphine needed to be titrated up. Or that he needed some oxycodone, or fentanyl, or anything else, whatever his liver and kidney functions would allow, whatever would work. Well-trained medical students had asked him to describe the pain: Gnawing? Crampy? Piercing? Colicky? Joey was able to answer at first, but at some point, with the increasing intensity, he could no longer find the perfect word, nor did it really matter. When he was still in the mood to indulge these persistent questions he described it as like having shards of broken glass, or a mace, embedded in his entrails, but as soon as he felt content with his descriptions, new adjectives, new metaphors would become necessary. Emaciation, anorexia, pain, jaundice— cancer had clearly taken full control of the board and was proudly announcing its hostile takeover.

It was my classmate Rina who had introduced me to this particular hue of yellow, way back in Grade 2. Rina was known for her big personality, not one to shy away from recitations or extracurricular activities. She was also a regular on the "Noisy List", so everyone felt her absence when she started missing classes. There were rumors, mostly circulated among mothers waiting at the school gate, that Rina had been hospitalized for a mysterious illness. One day she came back to school her usual jolly self, but we noticed that her eyes and skin were bright yellow. Nobody thought much about it, just that she was yellow.

The teachers started talking, saying she had hepatitis B, which, they insisted quite erroneously, was something that she got from eating too much cheese curls. Cheese curls were bright yellow, hence the yellow eyes. Three days later we noticed that her cheeks became puffy, and that her belly was getting distended. We assumed that she was getting fat. That she was getting better. Over the next few days she started getting yellower, forcing the canteen staff to get rid of all the bright yellow sitchiria and every yellow food, for that matter, like pancit palabok. Rina stopped attending class altogether. We asked our adviser, Mrs. Bahuta, if she had any news on what happened to her. Rina is dead, she said, and did we review our pronouns and adverbs?

None of the adults would talk about her, our queries getting quickly dismissed with irritation. We got the sense that there was blame going around—on Rina's mother for making poor dietary choices, the canteen for serving the food, Rina for such ravenous consumption of food color that had saturated her blood. Our classmate Hobill said that the mother had insisted on Sunny orange and bright yellow pospas getting served during the wake. I would never forget the look of Rina's eyes, and how it portended her death. Years later we would learn of a new word that describes this color:

jaundice. In med school we would learn another word—anasarca—or the generalized edema associated with a failing liver.

Joey seemed worried when I excused myself to call my consultant. We agreed to hold off on the scheduled treatment. The extent of the liver injury from cancer made it dangerous to do chemo. The liver was already too sick to process the drugs, and insisting on it would be disastrous. Joey and Mike agreed that they would stay in the hospital for a while to optimize pain control. Having gradually come to terms with the cancer over the past years Joey was ready to lay out the final version of his advanced directives. He died at home a few weeks later. One of his final requests was that his make-up be thick enough to cover the sallow-pale-jaundiced tone that his corpse would soon take. But not thick enough, he had instructed Mike sternly, to make him look like a deranged mutant clown whore.

Carcass

IN THE MIDST OF ALL THE BITTERNESS over the tragedy that our lives had turned into, Smoketh and I whined and wished that we were born with a silver spoon rammed down our throats. We weren't really impoverished, and we didn't want to sound ungrateful for our blessings, but as fellows-in-training it was imperative to maintain a veneer of distress. Smoketh herself was born with a bejeweled platinum spoon, a set of deluxe cutlery, and a coconut plantation, but covered in the grime of fellowship and recent financial setbacks, she was still in the mood to commiserate.

In the middle of writing our fellowship research papers, we tried to imagine the fantastic lives of our med school classmates, they who had sprung out of their mothers' uteri sucking on such silver spoons, and gone through the entire course of their lives with the darn spoons still epoxied to their hard palates. We combed through their social media accounts, oooh-ing and aaah-ing at each travel photo, further exacerbating our envy and self-loathing. Patricia, who was an internal medicine resident in New York, was rolling on the beaches of Ibiza. A few more seconds of painful scrolling and we saw Mario on a yacht, sipping martini. Tammy was having wine and marbled steak with a hot physician... in Chicago. Even Mel who was eating pita bread in Polo Loco Megamall made us hate ourselves. From our very narrow vantage point, which was nothing more than a pinhole, these smart, beautiful people never seemed to have experienced a rough patch in their lives. Good thing we weren't competitive in med school and in life. Because clearly, they won.

"*Yayaman kaya tayo sa pagdodoktor,*" Smoketh inquired as she downed a glass of calorific cocktail. We weren't sure of the answer, and we didn't want to stress over our precarious futures any further. Research, alcohol, and other people's social media were a terrible combination, like asking someone to dunk your head in a vat of boiling water. We turned off those two horrible applications— Instagram and RevMan—and opted to go back to writing on our online journals. To rant! To whine! To spread despair!

Smoketh's blog readership has slowly been growing, her reader count now up to four. A month ago I beseeched her to document her travails as a nephrology fellow.

"What do you find thrilling in your life right now?" I asked, with the tone of a self-appointed guru.

"Whenever I see golden urine rushing out of the foley catheter and sloshing beautifully into the urine bag," she said.

"Then write about it!" I yelled, a little more OA than I had intended.

The excitement made us happy and sad at the same time.

In college I had assumed that I would pursue writing as a profession. Maybe work for an advertising agency by day to pay the bills, then write my pretentious post-modern novel at night. I had 3 units of free elective, so I enrolled in a Creative Writing course on Short Fiction. Our teacher was this tall charming guy named Mr. Farcon, whom my friend Melissa Skullky said had been hitting on her. Come to think of it, I never got to ask Melissa if they ever went out for coffee, but from all the gossip going around it seemed that Mr. Farcon was a serial dater.

And he bragged about these dates in class, keeping us entertained for hours. His dating stories had unintentionally given us pointers on exposition: how to exaggerate without seeming too unbelievable, and how to always emerge in the end as the good guy. My classmates were a wild mix, and having such eccentric people from all over the university was already worth the price of admission. There was Miss Janine, a very articulate Mass Com major who always regaled us with tales of promiscuity in the Sunken Garden. Frankly her tales sounded suspiciously made-up, or maybe I was just envious, as the only people who ever paid me any attention in the Sunken Garden were the aggressive evangelists of the Metro Manila Christian Church. There was Mrs. Buenaventura, a retired government employee in her early 60's, who had enrolled in the class to deal with empty nest. Her husband, a retired family physician, had paid for her tuition fees as an anniversary gift. Varicella Zosterina, a Communication Arts major, always dished out dirt on her supposedly vicious mother-in-law. While waiting for Mr. Farcon she would stand in front of the class and say the vilest things about her. We thought that it was a mildly amusing schtick at first, until she started bawling about intestate and land grabbing issues.

Among my classmates, the most vocal during recitations was Jayson, a fine arts major, who really tried to internalize being an "artist" by hating everything. For him each story we were required to read, at some level, reeked of "intellectual masturbation". Everything was either lacking in or indulging in too much "pathos", "ethos", "bathos", or "gravitas", as if no one could get just the right amount of it. I didn't even know what those concepts were. But my favorite classmate was Alexander Crocodilium, a gaunt bespectacled guy with long, silky hair. He always looked stoned. The main character in one of his stories is a thin, stoned guy who goes on a road trip with his friends while The Cranberries' Dreams is blaring on repeat. Unbeknownst to these friends he has been planning to kill them with the katana hidden in the trunk of his car.

Towards the end of the semester, we turned in our short stories written under a pseudonym, and copies were distributed to everyone. We read each story at home and critiqued them in class the next day. The identity of the writer was then revealed at the end of the session. Most of the time the identity was anything but a surprise, like when "Persephone" wrote about an evil mother-in-law who was a closeted cannibal. My short story was about a guy who looked very young for his age. He goes to seedy "pene-kula" houses in Cubao just to see if the guard will let him in without checking his ID. His romantic interest, Stella, has never loved him other than as a younger brother, which infuriates him to no end. I can't quite remember how it ended. I think he stuck his head in a toilet bowl in protest. It got some rather mixed to poor reviews from the class, and as I listened to their vile criticisms, I reveled at the feeling of being a tortured, misunderstood soul.

One story, written under the pseudonym Chummy, was particularly skewered. Her story, *Prayers Can Move Mountains*, is a 15-page tragedy that revolves around family members participating in loud altercations, followed by unrelenting apologies. It was a tedious read. Chummy had taken the professor's advice to "describe even the things inside your character's pockets" quite literally, so we knew that her main character has shoulder-length hair, red bestida, black Haruta shoes, and a red handkerchief with tiny, yellow flowers. It would have been perfectly fine, but she had described all twelve characters with equal intensity. Her choice of exposition was setting up a series of scenes in the dining area, where everyone is given the opportunity to dredge up past hurts. They are always eating together, and they are always fighting. The story had potential to be epic, but it was a difficult one to slog through. Too many adjectives were crammed into every available slot, as if we weren't allowed to imagine what anything looked like.

"I'm sorry, but it's quite a snooze-fest. Not necessarily bad *naman* but it is *so boring*, like a journal on electrophoresis," Isis Santos said with a sheepish look on her face. The rest weren't as kind.

"That's really awful," Jayson, the guy who hated everything, bellowed. "I fell asleep reading it. Took me a few days to get through the description of how the kitchen looked like!"

As soon as the fangs were out, it was only a matter of time before we tried one-upping each other in viciousness, as though we were competing to be the snarkiest literary critic. Allan Santos: "Ranking in terms of quality, among all the twenty stories, the placement of 'Prayers Can Move Mountains' will be… in the garbage bin". Trinia: "One of the main characters, Attorney Trixie, seems to be fighting with everyone in the family. I thought her eventual demise was being foreshadowed. I suggest turning this family drama into a murder mystery."

Otto Von Hurrman, synthesizing everyone's thoughts: "*Napakaboring po.*"

"Anyone else?" Mr Farcon smiled. "If none, may we ask who Chummy is?"

We all watched in wide-eyed terror as the nice elderly woman suffering from empty nest, Mrs. Buenaventura, stood up, hands semi-raised, a guilty look on her face.

"Uhm, actually ma'am, *maayos naman po,*" Jayson said quickly. "I think some of the fat can be trimmed, but in general I actually like it *po!*"

"I actually agree, *ha,*" Varicella Zosterina stammered. "In particular the atmosphere was well-developed *po!*"

"I like the archetype of the strong Filipino mother that Attorney Trixie represents,"—or something crappy like that—was my contribution to the major undoing extravaganza.

All this time Mr. Farcon was watching us, nefariously smiling, enjoying the view of these sorry vultures frantically attempting to put the carcass back together.

The 50th Degree

ONE OF MY CHARITY PATIENTS with metastatic osteosarcoma, Miss Tina, called me on the phone at 2 am to report that her hacking cough had gotten worse. She was burning up. Having recently bombarded her with intense chemotherapy, this drove me insane. I immediately considered febrile neutropenia, the condition where the blood count plummets to dangerously low levels, making her vulnerable to all sorts of nasty infections. On the very first day of fellowship one of our consultants had drilled in us the importance of panicking when a post-chemotherapy patient develops fever. I had totally imbibed this fear and never let it go, resulting in constant anxiety, hyper-cautiousness, the propensity to over-advise, and other mental health issues.

The PGH emergency room being what it was, I was afraid that for Tina, jumping head first into the ER would be like having to face a Grand Jury, or at least a jury in a reality talent competition. Only she was up against the more spectacular aortic dissection, organophosphate poisoning, and a blast injury to the face. She could definitely benefit from someone acting as her lawyer, an advocate, a cheerleader, a fixer. After years of training in this hospital we knew that our Emergency Room could only accommodate those in the class AB. There were so many patients flocking in from all parts of the country that at times the resources could only accommodate those who are really, genuinely, legitimately AB, i.e., *Agaw Buhay*.

There won't be much sleep tonight, I thought, as I braced myself for a series of phone calls. I called Dr. Jean Luke, the ER resident, introduced myself as an oncology fellow, and asked if the patient could be accommodated. I would be happy to admit her, the very sleepy Jean Luke said, "But there are currently twenty backlogs in the emergency room, sir, some of them already waiting for four days to get transferred to the wards. If the Medicine wards can probably free-up…"

So, I called Kimmy, the Medicine resident-on-duty tasked to look for beds, and happily discovered that there were, in fact, only four patients waiting for a Medicine bed. The other sixteen in the queue were from other services such as surgery and orthopedics, so there was a chance that I could get Tina a Golden Ticket to a bed. But the other four were such strong contenders: pneumonia in the elderly, congestive heart failure, diabetic foot, and a patient for dialysis, so Miss Tina still had to be as stellar as possible. The first person to impress: Kimmy.

Back when I was an internal medicine resident Kimmy was a student under my service. I was quite certain that I had been a nice resident, having sown seeds of kindness specifically so I could reap the fruits of *utang na loob* years later. I was nice, and I intended to collect. I mean Kimmy had been a bit remiss with some of her responsibilities as a student, oftentimes turning in the census late in the afternoon when I had already finished my rounds. And yet I had been, like, super cool about it, in contrast to Dr. Virulina who would write obnoxious things on the chart like "Student-in-charge to please refer to ophthalmology without fail!". So, I thought it wouldn't be too pushy to ask for something that was, strictly speaking, not even classifiable as a favor.

"Oh, hi Kimmy! This is Will, Med Onco fellow, *you're second year resident na pala!* I hope you're not too toxic. Listen, I have a patient who might be having pneumonia in the immunocompromised host... uhmm... is there a chance, that, you know, I could get a bed..."

"Back of the line, smart guy," Kimmy snapped. That's not exactly what she said, but I thought I'd have fun and make her seem more cartoonish than she really was to justify my rather immature, self-righteous annoyance.

I informed Tina that she might need to get admitted in other hospitals instead, which made her burst into tears. In the spirit of the concept of "*Agaw Buhay*", it dawned on me to ask her daughter to take Tina's blood pressure. It was dangerously low at 70/50.

"That's great!" I said, which must have made me sound like a total psychopath.

I quickly called up the ICU resident-in-charge, Oswald, who said that they had two vacant beds, and that so far there were no other referrals raring to grab it. I then talked to the service senior Anna Romanova and again Jean Luke, and they both agreed that Tina was deserving of an ICU bed. Having assembled a team composed of Oswald, Anna Romanova, and Jean Luke I felt like I had succeeded in my quest for social justice.

Take that, Kimmy!

For all my misplaced irritation at Kimmy I completely understood where she was coming from. I had been there. I knew the feeling of getting dropped smack in the middle of the emergency room with all your senses getting assaulted simultaneously—relatives asking for updates, seniors asking for more updates, the stench of a gangrenous breast cancer that a grandmother had been keeping secret for years, the wet diabetic foot doused with a concoction of Zonrox and vinegar, everybody's dried sweat, Wendy's Biggie Iced Tea accidentally knocked over the charts, and so on. So in the face of vexing, extraneous stimuli that would emerge without warning, like a fellow who viewed things as a reality competition, you wouldn't really have time to pore through your personal records of who had been nice three years ago. Everyone would just look like a nasty, self-important Dr. Virulina.

Years ago, in one of my ER duties as an internal medicine resident, I remember having to drop a call from an irate cardiology fellow when a patient, Mr. Tunggol, had been wheeled-in. Mr. Tunggol looked well at first, but as soon as he stood up from his stretcher, bright red blood went splattering on the floor, seemingly from his anus. This was followed by projectile vomiting of pure blood which soaked everyone's shoes. I hadn't seen such catastrophic, synchronous hemorrhaging from both ends before, so I ordered the procurement of blood for transfusion and somatostatin drip on the chart. Stat! (canned laughter)

Things being what they were at the time, we knew that my emergency order wouldn't come to life on its own. The somatostatin wouldn't magically appear and reconstitute itself. All the nurses were busy attending to other things and no relatives were in sight. The drug wasn't available in the pharmacy. I had no choice but to dash across Taft and buy the medication from a commercial pharmacy, making sure to keep the receipts for reimbursement from the department funds. On my phone I saw five missed calls from the cardiology fellow, who must be tearing his hair in annoyance by now. In a dark corner near Wendy's Taft I saw my friends Chepoy and Cassandra laughing and drinking enormous cups of iced tea and smoking their lungs out. I died of envy. While waiting for the stoplight to turn red Chepoy saw me and yelled, "Will! Wait! I have *chika*!"

"Later!" I yelled back. Come to think of it, I never got to learn what the gossip was.

Even as the somatostatin was being hooked, and the cardiology call was still ringing unanswered, in came patient Jerome T, who was being readmitted for pulmonary congestion. Everybody knew Jerome. He had been in and out of the hospital for the past five years. His heart was about ready to give up this time, as he never had enough funds for possible life-saving valvular replacement. Jerome was immediately followed by a girl on a stretcher, with a nasogastric tube full of activated charcoal rammed up her nostril. Cyanide poisoning. I was finally able to answer the cardiology fellow's call with profuse apologies, and he sounded pretty incensed. I was ready to get the third degree and listen to a longish lecture on how I had neglected a patient with heart attack leading to an audit-worthy mortality, but apparently, he just wanted to ask if he had left his house keys in the ward when we were talking there that morning.

The patient hemorrhaging from both ends, Mr. Tunggol, was an old patient of my batchmate Lochia. Mr. Tunggol was known to have recurrent bleeding ulcers, but the latest endoscopy had demonstrated a tumor. They were still waiting for the biopsy result, but they suspected that it could be an aggressive form of gastric cancer. That night, despite the multiple blood transfusions and every medical management available, the tumor bled massively. He went into cardiac arrest, commonly referred to as "code". We eventually revived him from the code, but he had kept me awake all night, having to run for blood, respirator, more somatostatin, referrals to the other services, and so on. I was able to beg for an ICU bed for the patient.

I was finally able to nap at the call room at around 7 am, only to be awoken a few minutes later by the high-pitched voice of Lochia nagging the ER doctor whom he thought had failed to do initial stabilization. Lochia was definitely giving him not just the third degree, but the 49th-degree. Lochia had just come in that morning, and I had not yet formally endorsed all the events. I did not really understand the whole scenario that got Lochia all fired-up, but I woke up to this nag:

"*Dahil sa tagal ng blood*," Lochia yelled, "*Namatay yung patient! Namatay!*" The word "*namatay*" woke me up to a start, so I immediately pulled Lochia aside in the middle of the heated phone conversation and groggily whispered, in bad morning breath—

"*Lochia, hindi namatay. Nag-code lang, pero na revive. Buhay pa sya!*"

Not about to have his momentum halted by this, and with no intention of taking any of his proud vitriol back, Lochia went back to the phone receiver and resumed his 49th-degreeing, albeit with a reset—

"*Dahil sa tagal ng blood, nag-code sya! Nag code siya! Nag-code!*" After placing the receiver down, *I* then received the 50th degree, for not updating him on time.

Anti-Dugyot Support Group

IN MY MANY YEARS AS A TRAINEE I had received multiple memos from the administration ordering me to wear my doctorly white coat in the hospital premises at all times. It was for my own good, without the coat I would be mistaken for trash. If a memo could be given to those with horrible grooming practices, I would have received a pile of those as well. More important than the administrative reminders though, were my friends' admonition that it was time to update my wardrobe. We were no longer tie-dye wearing, isaw-munching UP denizens of the 90's. Still, I would insist on donning a collarless Batman t-shirt, jeans, and Crocs in my daily rounds at the Cancer Institute.

While studying one night at the Shrine Motherfucker Café, who should I see walking in but my friend Dr. Margaret Burnz. For someone who was still in residency training she looked pretty well-kempt, her hair lush and full of life, her face glowing and without pores. After a few quick hello's I asked her, being the chief resident of the Section of Dermatology, "Hey Burnz, how do I pulverize these dark inflammatory zits?"

In my old age I assumed that wrinkles, facial sagging, and liver spots would edge out acne, but I was wrong. Just this morning I witnessed two gigantic pustules springing to life. Actually, they were more like boils containing lab-mutated insects, like the ones in the wonderful X-Files episode "Faciphaga Emasculata". I attributed the breakouts not only to stress which had been shooting through the roof in the past few months, but also to the multi-drug resistant hospital bacteria and fungi that had decided to nest on my face.

Margaret Burnz wrote an entire acne regimen on a tissue paper. After washing my face with a mild cleanser I was to slather it with extreme antibiotics. Then I should sit in front of an electric fan for five minutes, to let it dry out. This would be followed with the application of a powerful anti-acne gel, and a dollop of cream on top of it. Finally I should smear a thick coat of mega-sunblock on my face, and with a kitchen ladle mix everything into a slurry. Even as Margaret Burnz was explaining the process and the expected results and the pharmacology of it all I knew I couldn't comply. That I would just let the lesions dry up on their own, creating dark spots and craters.

"*Nakakatamad*," I whined. "It will take a lot of getting used to. *Pag naliligo ako, isang Safeguard bar lang ang dala ko sa banyo*. For use as soap *and* shampoo."

To which Margaret Burnz glowered and screamed, "*San ka nakatira, sa construction site*? That will destroy your hair! Eeew!" She lit a cigarette and started blowing smoke through her nose in infuriation.

"At least my hairline is intact," I retorted. "I don't have much in terms of beauty, but I'm glad I'm not balding. At least not yet. I intend to keep my wild, bushy, itchy hair for as long as I can. By the way, have you noticed that my hair ends up looking like an aardvark whenever I insist on shaping it with wax?"

Margaret didn't care one bit if my head looked like an aardvark or a tyrannosaurus. She was gingerly looking at my shoulders, the white flecks on my black shirt making her wince.

"*Pag kinakamot ko ang ulo ko nahuhulog 'yang mga white flecks na 'yan,*" I confessed.

Margaret exploded: "*Ang tawag dyan, balakubak!*" She took back the tissue containing the acne regimen and added dandruff shampoo on the therapeutic protocol. It was decided: I needed help not just with my face, but also with over-all grooming, hygiene, personality development, and other things I should have learned in Grade 4.

As if on cue, who should walk in but Waylon Smith to save Margaret Burnz from dealing with this fashion and hygiene disaster by herself. Waylon was an internal medicine resident. He and his batchmates were known for dressing well and looking neat on a daily basis, not just during conferences held in airconditioned halls. After Margaret's reportage Waylon severely rebuked me and gave some pointers on how to dress properly:

The shoulder line of your shirt should be two centimeters above your shoulders. You should own one pair each of rubber shoes, brogue, oxford, and loafers. Corollarily... Dump those dreadful, dreadful Crocs!

Your pants should be mid-waist. The waist is very near the umbilicus. Mid-waist, on the other hand, is that line made through the anterior superior iliac spine. (Waylon demonstrated how the pants should accommodate the crotch by cupping his own crotch with both hands, and jumping up and down)

You should own at least two kinds of perfume. Use them on alternate days.

You should have well-developed traps, pectorals, and biceps so that your shirt fits well.

"I don't have well-developed pecs, but I have central obesity," I said. "And I used to go to the gym, for two months. Eight years ago!"

Not to be discouraged by my blank stares and head scratching, Waylon dutifully went on to share ten other nuggets of wisdom on grooming, but my favorite:

"If you plan to rotate your pants in a week, you should have at least three pairs—khaki, black, and blue. How many pairs of pants do you have Will? What's your rotating schedule, Will? They know if you just repeat your pants, Will, they know!"

They know? Who's they? I asked. The government? The military-industrial complex? The Zeta Reticulans? I knew I couldn't wisecrack my way out of this, so I had to confess my ultimate faux-pas to the fierce Miss Margaret Burnz and Mr. Waylon Smith. At this point they were already so revolted that cigarette smoke was violently billowing from all available orifices.

"Waylon, Burnz, the pair of jeans that I wear on Monday, is the same pair I wear until Friday!"

Waylon and Margaret choked, coughed, groped at the nearest stable furniture, and almost suffered severe inhalational injury. I tried to explain that I only do that because I'm too lazy to transfer the belt, wallet, and all the other stuff into a new pair every day, but this excuse did not fly at all.

Having sufficiently recovered, Mr. Waylon Smith and Miss Margaret Burnz decided that they would do their best to transform me into something that resembles a human being. They drafted a treaty, signed it, and committed themselves to be my willing sponsors in my 2013 Anti-Dugyot Support Group!

"First, we have to set our objectives and determine a peg." Waylon said excitedly. "What is your fashion goal?"

"My fashion goal is to be like…"

"Goals have to be S.M.A.R.T," Waylon reminded. "Specific, Measurable, Attainable…"

"My goal is to be like…"

"..Reliable, Time-bound…" Miss Margaret Burnz continued.

"Geraldine!" I declared. "I want to be like Geraldine Zamora!"

Final Threats

AS WE WERE WALKING BACK to the hospital from an oncology conference, I was re-telling a fifth-hand story to my fellowship batchmates Carina, Eric, and Alanis Cornucopia. It was a fascinating saga—actually, a nasty gossip—involving hospital personalities, narrated in my characteristic manner of using as many vulgar terms as I could possibly cram in. It seemed like a hilarious story at the time, but now I can only cringe and hope that nobody was eavesdropping. To my batchmates' credit they had all gotten used to humoring me in my pathetic attempts at doing stand-up comedy. But this time, after all the courtesy laughter had ended, Alanis Cornucopia grabbed me by my shirt collar and said, *"baka may makarinig, gusto mo bang hindi maka-graduate!"*

This slapped me back to reality. Since then, I've decided to maintain a veneer of being respectable, never to be caught off-guard mumbling a throwaway *"pota!"* at the slightest provocation, such as when I accidentally knock a stapler off the clinic table. Graduation from fellowship is just a few months away. I don't care if the inspirational speaker tells us that "graduation is not the end... but only the beginning," for me it will be the absolute, enjoyable, delicious end. Over one decade of studying is barreling through to the finish, and nobody wants a random joke, videotaped and taken out-of-context, to turn everything into a total disaster.

We are acutely aware, in the spirit of catastrophizing, that many horrific things can go wrong: I can snap and go ballistic in the middle of the clinic, be involved in an ill-advised sexual liaison by the fire escape, or absentmindedly administer a breast cancer chemo regimen to a patient with colon cancer. All of these will give me online infamy and disqualify me from graduation, but worst of all, they might win me a stint in prison. This is not an irrational fear. We've heard of trainees who had cut the wrong tissue or made a poor administrative decision on their last year of training and were quickly dismissed from the hospital.

The last time I was placed at risk of not graduating happened way back in high school. While sucking on a santan nectar during recess my classmate, Bort, approached me. He had a sinister look on his face that seemed to say "I am morally above you this time. I'm bringing you to the office!"

"Me?" I exclaimed, pretending to be shocked. He explained that no less than the Directress Sister Maria Lorenda Trinidad delos Santos Almazora had asked him to drag me to her office, much to his delight. I had already gotten into trouble earlier that year. As a proactive stance the student government had one day decided to pass around a survey that asked a question of extreme socio-economic importance: What brand of mineral water do you want to be available in the canteen? For some reason I wrote "Cave Water." Until now I don't know why I did that. It wasn't particularly witty or funny or even smart-alecky. Maybe because I was due for an unnecessary rebellion, a pathetic one at that. A few days later the student escorts raided all the rooms, rounding up all the students who did not take the survey seriously. While we were detained in the Executive Chairperson's Office I asked Mariah, "*Ano ba kasi sinulat mo?*" She said, "Who Cares Mineral Water."

Bort dropped me off at the office. He cackled with imagined superiority as he walked away with thirty pieces of silver or a plea bargain for all his past transgressions. Sister Maria Lorenda Trinidad etc. told me sternly that she wasn't too pleased with the editorial I had written in the latest issue of the school paper. As the editor-in-chief I reported that some public-school teachers were selling longganisa to their students, having seen it firsthand while doing catechism in the nearby communities. It would reflect poorly on the catechism program, she scolded, and the school organ is not the proper venue for such impetuous reportage no matter how valid it might seem. We would look like these snooty, self-important assholes looking down on them after we had been welcomed with open arms. In retrospect, now in my advanced age, I see the wisdom in her advice. My editorial was nothing more than manufactured drama written in an attempt to give life to a school paper peppered with news reports on who had won what quiz bee, and juvenile poems about not losing hope because we can make it through the rain. I apologized profusely, telling Sister Trinidad that it will never happen again. On the very next issue I wrote in big bold letters on a filler area: SUPPORT THE

FREEDOM OF THE PRESS! It was very Briony Tallis, that petulant young girl from Ian Mc Ewan's *Atonement* who inflates her own importance by creating drama everywhere.

Drama or not, taking control of the school paper was one of my few happy memories in high school. They could have their Citizens' Army Training and Student Council positions, I could write whatever I wanted in the broadsheet like a total dictator. Some members of the staff weren't really taking their positions seriously, and I happily took their jobs. Nobody wanted to do the lay-out, I did it myself like a maniac. Nobody wanted to write about pop culture, I wrote articles upon articles about The X-Files that nobody ever read! The only thing I never touched was my friend Rex's serial The Vicar Of Christ, a short story about the Pope and the conspiracies surrounding his papacy. At one point I was so consumed with editorial power that I was a few steps away from renaming the paper from The Lily to *The Willy*. Even my friends Japt, Rex, Raquel, and Ruth Marks thought that it was a horrible idea. We decided, instead, to come up with a lampoon issue of the paper, featuring no-holds-barred, extremely lewd stories in the vein of Xerex Xaviera. Unlike Xerex, though, we didn't resort to euphemisms such as "*tarugo*" and "*hiyas*". Obviously, it was only meant to be shared among friends.

One afternoon we were all laughing like idiots as we were reading together the third issue of the lampoon hot off the presses (i.e., Microsoft Publisher). Our teacher, Mr. Sharlo Kalilis, was not too pleased with this, and demanded that we surrender whatever we were reading. We were a month away from graduation, we had already been accepted in good universities, we had lasted this long without getting into real trouble. But as Mr. Kalilis was walking towards Ruth Marks, who was clutching in his palms the most disgusting issue of the paper, we knew we were finished.

"No," Ruth Marks said firmly when Mr. Kalilis stretched his hand out to snatch the paper.

"No, Sir," Ruth Marks repeated. He folded the paper and kept it in his pocket, much to our collective relief. But Mr. Kalilis would not be denied. He was about to grab Ruth Marks' hands, but Ruth Marks quickly stuffed the paper in his mouth and started munching on it.

We owe our lives, our careers, our entire future, to Ruth Marks.

Punctuate It With A Slurp,
Why Don't You

OUR RESIDENCY BATCHMATE, Christy, stormed into the call room one afternoon visibly distressed. A resident from another department, Marjorie, was apparently annoyed at her for requesting an additional laboratory test for pre-operative evaluation, and they had gotten into a heated exchange witnessed by everyone in Ward B. As with any altercation in the hospital, Christy had two options: A) take the high road and be totally civil about it, maybe confront her with grace and diplomacy in the presence of our superiors, file an incident report if necessary, or B) do none of those things and just rant to anyone who will listen. In the hospital most of the backbiting happens in the residents' call room, where everybody sheds off the image of a subservient trainee and yells the most cathartic profanities. The batchmates, of course, take the role of patronizing enablers, always ready with platitudes that will tide someone over the rant-worthy event. Sometimes they also give legitimate, sane advice.

The sane advice would have been for Christy to file an incident report, so obviously we told her that it would be a pointless exercise. And really, how would anybody find a common time to meet with the chief residents and the training officers of two major departments.

"Maybe Marjorie has also moved on by now," I said.

I was wrong. The very next day Marjorie accosted Christy in the Nurses' Station and started yelling in her face. The patients, their relatives, and nurses all flocked to the brewing drama, and gleefully witnessed a young, mildly pretty doctor having a total meltdown. Not to be outdone in the meltdown department, Christy gave Marjorie some choice words of her own. But very quickly Christy's voice began to falter, and she started stammering, shivering. She had rehearsed what she would say should this sordid sequel happen, but no rehearsal was enough to ward off the rampage of Majorie. Christy lost control of the situation and tears started to well up her eyes. She dashed out of the wards in shame.

As Christy was buying siopao in the canteen, imagining that Marjorie was still in the wards gloating at her easy surrender, who should she hear yakking on her ear but Marjorie. It wasn't an echo, a colony of bees, nor her imagination—apparently Marjorie had been following her ever since she walked out of the wards! The absurdity of being hounded by a long-playing rant as they were passing by the Spine Unit, the parking lot, and out into Padre Faura was not lost on Christy, but Marjorie still had a lot on her chest. Christy decided on the only logical course of action: she ran.

"We were wrong! You should file an incident report!" we screamed while playing Boggle in the call room. "You should talk to the consultants, tell them that Marjorie's a horrific bitch, describe all the events..."

"Or how about we sit down and talk to her diplomatically?" Aids said as he hit an imaginary tennis ball with his Wii controller.

"She does not deserve diplomacy!" Chifoo insisted.

"Maybe there are complex psycho-social factors…" Aids went on.

The most remarkable aspect of the story was Marjorie's rather cartoonish effort in tagging along while expertly spewing expletives. We were astonished, and frankly a little bit impressed, at her loony persistence. We imagined that she was standing outside our locked call room right that moment, delivering an oratorical piece with fervor. From Christy's account of the events we couldn't figure out what got Marjorie so fired up, but the most plausible explanation was that Marjorie had gotten into trouble with her seniors for overlooking details that delayed her patient's surgery. We wanted to tell ourselves that, because the alternative explanation would require us to judge Marjorie's sanity, and accept Aids' dissertation on the complex interplay of stressful environmental factors, unhealthy working conditions, and poor mental health.

It was a lot of work.

We had forgotten all about the Marjorie incident immediately after that. Newer, juicier call room intrigue must have quickly diverted our chaotic fancy. By the time we graduated from residency Marjorie and Christy had already become friends, and this non-issue would not even merit mention in our batch reunions.

I was reminded of this unsavory incident with Marjorie years later when I was already a medical oncology fellow. Patient Roy G was admitted at the Cancer Institute, and as his oncology fellow-in-charge I was really hoping that I could resume his chemotherapy. His metastatic testicular tumor seemed to be acting more aggressively than usual, and his pulmonary symptoms were getting worse. The fever, anorexia, and the kidney problems were complicating things, so at the very start I had the other fellows from nephrology, infectious disease, and palliative care come in to help. We had become Roy's de facto team, and I only needed to text them whenever he was admitted.

Rose, the infectious disease doctor, happily revealed that the viral tests and other cultures were negative. She cleared Roy for chemo without any concern for infections going wild. Barbie, the palliative care expert, laid out her advice on nutrition and pain control. But it had already been three days, and the kidney doctor Blessie still hadn't made an appearance. I finally caught her leisurely drinking Jekah Juice while I was withdrawing from the ATM.

"Hi! Blessie hi!" I cheerily said as I ran after her. I was faking it. I wasn't really feeling cheerful. I was extremely annoyed, because I only knew of one way to deal with such situations and I hated it: fawn.

Blessie immediately put on a veneer of being extremely busy, pretending to look at her wristwatch, then quickly going through a thick sheaf of papers. It was obvious that she was not happy to see me at all.

"Sorry Bles, I know you're super busy, did you get my text?" I enthused, the feigned overfamiliarity making me nauseous. "Roy is already in the Cancer Institute. He's getting thinner, *ha*. Can you see him today?"

"Oh, yes I got all your texts," she said. "But you still need to fill up a referral form before I can see him. It's in the office." She started running towards the elevator. "You can get the form on the 6th floor, and make sure you fill up everything. The table must include the serial electrolytes, all the creatinine's…"

"But… but you already have all of those on file…"

Blessie walked even faster. I tried to catch-up, making sure that she couldn't escape. Good thing there was a long queue to the elevator.

"I need to see them in writing."

"But I filled up a referral form in his last admission. The only update is that his creatinine is now 2.2."

"I need it in *writing,*" she declared with finality, punctuated with an audible slurp of her Jekah Juice.

"They are in writing all right… in the patient's chart!" I glowered. "You need to go to the patient's room today, the chart is there, the things you need to know are there! In writing!"

I suddenly felt the nefarious specter of Marjorie looming over me. A vicious, unedited rant was about to let loose: "The patient has been waiting for your inputs for days!" to be followed by "Your demands are unnecessary!" which would climax with an emotionally manipulative and totally embarrassing, "Blessie, I thought we were friends!"

But I decided to keep those sanctimonies to myself. I knew I had to be mature about it. I tried to compartmentalize my thoughts, and reflected: maybe Blessie is going through something, a personal struggle, a break-up, an acute hemorrhoidal attack. Too much time had been wasted on being angry, time I could have used talking to

Roy. Blessie deserves a conversation, not a tirade, not a lashing, not insults, because we are all adults, and I am taking the high road.

But the most important reason—heck, the only real reason—for taking the high road: in one month I would be graduating from fellowship, and I was not about to lose my mind and scream like a loon in an elevator queue. Nope, I would not be the blabbering, high-strung idiot in the lobby of the biggest hospital in the country, caught on camera, screaming like I should be put in a straitjacket!

Fine, fine, fine, I mumbled, stomping my feet. Fine! I'm filling up the referral form. Fine! But I'll make my handwriting as horrible as I can! Also, I will tell your chief fellow! I will! I will tell on you! I will…!

Blessie traipsed into the elevator, empty juice cup in hand, not a care in the world.

That Blasted Room

WHILE WAITING FOR A FRIEND at the Shrine Motherfucker Café
I decided to go through my phone directory to hunt down patients
I had not seen in a while. It was always convenient to write "lost
to follow up" on patients' records, and consequently blame poverty,
society, and our horrific healthcare system, but there was always the
option to be a little bit more proactive by texting a simple reminder
to patients who had gone AWOL. While this might be interpreted as
a pre-emptive way of avoiding guilt, or a shocking act of altruism, it
was really more out of fear from our mentors. Years of training had
effectively instilled in us the necessity of going the extra ten miles in
patient care, or else get called to present in a medical audit.

As I was scrolling through the list I realized in terror: Patient Ab -
died a few months ago from stage 4 pancreatic cancer. I only saw her
once, and then she decided to go back to Batanes where she eventually
succumbed. Patient Ap - driver of a doctor, died from metastatic colon
cancer. Patient At - small cell lung cancer that had metastasized to the
brain, died at home. Patient Be - responding well to treatment for liver
cancer, but he suddenly died from a stroke. Patient C - dead. Patient
Do - dead. Dead dead dead. Dead! I winced and cringed and felt
dreadful, and for the sake of my sanity stopped scrolling altogether.

Graduation from fellowship was just around the corner, but until
that point, I hadn't really formalized in my head how many of my
patients had died. In the hurly burly of training there was a tendency

to pronounce someone dead, feel sad, log the mortality in the census, then move on to the next tasks at hand. Seeing all the dead in the list made the pain more exquisite, the shame more concrete.

For sure there were numerous triumphs. Early-stage breast cancer patients, after recovering from the initial shock of alopecia, were mostly able to complete their chemotherapy cycles that culminated in wig-tossing graduation ceremonies. The lymphoma patients, once riddled with disseminated lumps, lived long, healthy lives. Even stage 4 patients experienced significant improvements in their quality of life—the tumors became smaller on CT scan, they regained their appetites. But the joy of these successes never seemed to counterbalance the hurts, nor did they intend to. Despite the very nature of cancer medicine, and the aphorism of "curing sometimes, relieving often, comforting always" there was always that youthful, foolish conceit that the default should be to cure.

I never really had nightmares, or actual preternatural experiences, involving patients who died at the Cancer Institute. If I had, it would probably be something akin to those post-Vietnam War movies, with an army of green, luminous ghosts standing together and collectively pointing their fingers at the amputated survivor suffering PTSD. One of my patients did send me a Facebook request for a duel in Bejeweled Blitz two months after she had died. I yelped when I saw the notification, then told her brother that it is a horrible idea to use his dead sister's account. Some of the recipients might get a heart attack.

Rumor had it that there were sightings of ghosts in the Cancer Institute. I hadn't seen one, whether it was a man with a neck mass, or a mastectomized woman floating by the fountain. We once thought we saw a nun. She turned out to be a real nun, neither floating nor headless, and a very nice one at that who gave us packed spaghetti. Still, my friend Helliza maintained that supernatural happenings had been reported through the years, and that I should never look at mirrors and other reflective surfaces anywhere in the area.

"Relatively few people have died in this building," I'd argued, "because the patients only stay here for elective treatment. As soon as they show any signs of dying, they are immediately wheeled to the wards or the ICU!". I sounded like Dana Scully. But even as I was rationalizing these things, I knew that if any building in the hospital could be a hotspot for ghosts and other mysterious creatures, the Cancer Institute would be it. There is no rule that prohibits patients from dying elsewhere, and then floating back to the place where they had created strong emotional connections.

The ghosts don't show up all the time, Helliza insisted. The most active ones are the ghosts of tiny, bald kids running around the halls, up and down the wide marble steps, into the garden. Some of them can be seen playing around the cement fountain, oftentimes using the swing or the seesaw. They are cute, but they can be quite unruly. They sometimes lose their way and they end up in the nearby Ophthalmology Building, where they get a kick out of poking sleeping interns. Like most ghosts they are not aware that they're dead, so after playtime they run back to their rooms. Then they put their arms up so the interns could extract their blood or put an intravenous line.

Our first exposure to the hallowed halls of the Cancer Institute was back during internship. One intern was tasked to go on duty every night to do the vital signs monitoring, blood extractions, and other bedside procedures on all the admitted patients. In one of my duties, I remember having a hard time finding a patient's room supposedly located near the elevator. I assumed it was just the exhaustion. I'd gone back and forth the hallway a few times, but I still could not locate the blasted room. I finally asked a senior nurse for help, and she grimaced. She told me to go back to the area near the elevator one more time. The room was there. It was so prominent, and the mahogany door was so huge, that it was very hard to miss. The nurse explained that this mysterious room likes playing tricks on new interns. Sometimes you will be staring at it, then you'll get distracted by a phone call, and when you turn around it's gone.

At the time I didn't find it particularly spooky. More than anything I found it very inconvenient. You already have a long list of tasks as an intern and the last thing you need is for a room to get all moody and appear-disappear for no reason whatsoever. A couple of friends then told me that they had a similar experience with The Vanishing Room. I suggested that the monitoring intern wear his shirt inside-out to counteract it, but it was supposedly applicable only to those getting lost in the forest under a *tikbalang*'s spell. Helliza suggested brighter lights.

The Club

SMOKETH HAS BEEN SPIRALING into a crowdsourcing frenzy, posting all sorts of things for sale, such as paintings, jewelries, and bonsai. Also up for grabs: ancient hand-held weaponry, bronze cannons, anitos, and creepy clown marionettes. She is not moonlighting as an antique dealer, she is just trying to get rid of all the things that have accumulated in their ancestral home. And those items barely scratch the surface. Her father has recently bequeathed her with keys to safety deposit boxes. She is yet to open any of them, an act that requires sufficient fortitude and a box of mood stabilizers.

People unfamiliar with Smoketh sometimes assume that she sensationalizes her *paninda* for online attention, until they walk into the attic of their mansion and bear witness to an extravaganza of spears, staves, knives, and swords for every occasion. Initially she didn't think that anybody would be interested, until men with very distinct and eccentric tastes started reaching out. One such aficionado of medieval melee weapons, Mikhail, PhD, has become a regular customer. He would raid the mansion, then go back to his wife with a crate of weapons, giggling like a ten-year-old boy who had scored a foil-cover comic book variant. Smoketh had the option to continue peddling him with more weapons, but she didn't want to be that kind of opportunistic businesswoman. Friendship took over. She has since banned Mikhail, PhD from the mansion, telling him that she would no longer be party to his Pre-malignant Hoarding Disorder (PhD).

"*Maawa ka sa asawa mo,*" she rebuked, in the most judgmental tone she could muster.

The most sensational item that she has put up for sale, the one that has gotten the most online attention and made us believe that there is no limit to the wonders that the mansion of Smoketh can offer, is a gold coffin.

"Anybody interested in a coffin?" her social media post says.

There were no takers—either for Halloween party use or for body disposal purposes—but there was a flurry of inquiries about the coffin's history. Smoketh explained that the recent spate of typhoons had caused terrible flooding inside their village, and the coffin needs to be evacuated after years of getting stuck in storage. When her mother was cremated ten years ago, Smoketh's dad decided to bring the coffin home. They stashed it in the basement, where it now sits beside a rusty contraption that we have always assumed is a medieval torture device.

Smoketh's mother died when we were still in internal medicine residency training. News of her rapidly deteriorating condition reached Smoketh while she was deep in her Neurology rotation. She was examining a patient's eye with an ophthalmoscope when her sister, Mabel, called her in panic and said that their mom needed to be hooked to triple inotropic support.

"Smoketh, her BP is going down, you have to come to the ICU right now."

"Go now, I'll cover for you," Rodel, a batchmate, reassured her.

Smoketh dropped everything and drove to Quezon City. Her mother died shortly thereafter from multiple complications from diabetes and heart disease.

As with any major family events, Smoketh was not very familiar with all the visitors coming to the wake. They were a huge clan with a wide reach in the medical and business communities, and on the first night the chapel was already filling up with sophisticated flower arrangements and mass cards.

"When I die, please make a donation to your charity of choice instead," she whispered, as we watched more flowers getting hauled in, now spilling out into the hallway. On the second night a huge truck had to come in to remove the flowers and make room for new deliveries.

"When I die please pick a good photo of me for display, preferably one where I'm in full travel regalia," was my request.

Guests came in droves, but one particular lady holding a paper cup by the water dispenser caught Smoketh's attention. Smoketh excitedly leaned forward to poke Mabel.

"*Ate, ate, ate, may celebrity!*" she whispered. "That woman near the water dispenser! It's Helen Gamboa!"

"*Tangek, hindi yan si Helen Gamboa,*" Mabel said after a quick glance. "That's Boots Anson-Roa!"

Smoketh would re-tell this tiny anecdote to the various guests throughout the course of the wake. A good icebreaker had landed on her lap, and she intended to exploit it. When it was no longer enough to sustain a long conversation with overstaying guests, she would simply ask them if they were familiar with the filmographies of Boots Anson-Roa and Helen Gamboa, and could they please list them from memory.

When we told Frichmond this story she said that she couldn't fathom how anybody could confuse the two fantastic veteran actresses for each other, Boots Anson-Roa having played the *ulirang* ina role in so many films and TV shows, and Helen Gamboa having a very distinct, unique beauty, unmistakable to those who had followed her weekly drama anthology in the 80's. She then let out a condescending laughter, saying:

"And besides, Smoketh, Helen Gamboa has been dead for years!"

"*Tangek, si Helen Vela yun,*" we chorused.

Smoketh went back to PGH the day after the cremation. She was eager to go back to work and learn more about Neurology. Strokes! Malignancies! Degenerative diseases! The toxicity in the wards would be good for her, she claimed, and so would gorging on processed, overpriced mall food. We trooped to Robinson's immediately after clinics, and indulged on huge Wham hamburgers, huge NY Fries, huge whipped cream-rich coffee, and huge White Hat Frozen Yoghurt. Nothing like death to excuse gluttony and cholesterol. Robert, one of Smoketh's fraternity brods, saw us pigging-out and waved. He approached our table and started to engage in small talk. They hadn't seen each other in months, as Robert had been busy being a house dad while his wife was training for residency.

In the middle of ranting about the cost of infants' clothes Robert suddenly paused and closed his eyes. We could hear the gears turning in his head, as if something urgent had just occurred to him. He was trying to remember something important, something that he felt he needed to tell Smoketh, a recent momentous event in her life that he sort of heard about but never could recall. Gears started squeaking, nuts and bolts chugged wildly, black industrial machine oil violently splattered out. Finally, it clicked—how could he possibly forget?

"Smoketh, oh my gosh I'm so sorry," he said with a half-smile, not yet fully convinced if he was remembering correctly. He placed his hand on Smoketh's shoulder and laughed nervously. "Umm, belated happy birthday?"

"No, but my mother has just died."

Robert was stunned.

Eeew, how insensitive, I thought, I guess you're not *that* close with Smoketh! My heart swelled with a sense of superiority and morbid amusement. I waited with bated breath how Robert would wrangle himself out of such awkwardness.

"Oh my," Robert started, his face now a mixture of shame and sorrow. "Welcome to the club, Smoketh."

The club?

"When my mom died from cancer last year," Robert continued, "I almost died from the pain myself. She never even got to meet her grandson. My sincerest condolences. It might take a while, but the wound will start to heal."

They then hugged each other, both tearing up.

Alleviations

WHEN I ENTERED MED SCHOOL in 2001, I rented an apartment located along the party district of Nakpil Street, and to my father's credit he correctly assumed that I would never jump out of my bedroom window straight into a mosh pit of strangers on a weeknight. At the time anyone in the mood to get wasted could escape to Malate and prowl its dark streets for pain and pleasure, long before the yuppies had abandoned it in search of cooler places to infiltrate. I recently walked along Nakpil Street and discovered that many of the bars had been replaced by Korean restaurants, although my friend Jay suspects that the new "bakery" might just be a front for secret rooms meant for high society gay orgies. The old apartment in 611 Nakpil is still there.

I had lived in that apartment for five years. I never really got to party, my exposure to the debauchery was limited to leisurely walks garbed in my *pambahay* while munching on overpriced kikiam. On my study breaks I would watch people gallivanting on the streets, with no envy or regret that I was wasting what should be the most sinful years of my youth. People-watching was therapeutic enough to wash off the muck of anatomy and biochemistry, and as I learned later on, one shouldn't make eye contact with random strangers unless hooking up was on the agenda. I once saw a friend dancing wildly with someone on a Friday night. They had just met that night, he said. They just stared at each other while he was leaning on a streetlamp, and that was it.

My room in 611 Nakpil was located on the second floor. My roommate, Jonafun, was a college student taking up speech pathology in UP Manila. Some nights I would smell something burning from the kitchen downstairs, and it would turn out to be dinner Jonafun was roasting on a hot plate. As the only undergrad in the house Jonafun would happily volunteer to do errands for us med students, such as paying the bills and cooking dinner on occasion.

My parents, Elena and Eddie, visited me in the apartment on weekends. On one such visit my father noted acrid smell rising from Jonafun's hot plate and decided that a comprehensive safety inspection was warranted. He couldn't care less for the walls of the microwave oven festering with coagulated gunk, nor for the cockroaches flittering out of the kitchen sink. But he got all apoplectic when he uncovered tangled cords from five computers competing for an overloaded power strip. At the end of his inspection, wisps of black smoke started to appear, and we couldn't figure out whether they were from the frayed electric wires of the hot plate, the ancient electric fan chugging and humming, or both. Only a matter of time before this house burns and explodes, my father said. Jonafun assumed that he would admonish us to buy fire extinguishers, and that would be the end of it.

"I had set up an emergency fire escape plan!" my father told us the following weekend. I retorted that an escape plan would be unnecessary, because we could easily run down the short flight of stairs. Fire and smoke would block the hallway, he insisted, or the wooden floors might come crashing down. On such eventuality there would be no other recourse but to exit through the window, and on cue he unveiled what he had been planning for the entire week. Hanging by the window sill was a thick roll of industrial rope, with one end tied and nailed to the head jamb of the window frame.

It's not a foolproof way to survive, I bitched. My skull might crack from the fall, or I might get knocked out from inhalational injury. He had expected this whininess. He opened the closet adjacent to the window, revealing a hard hat and a face mask. I might get too anxious and die from a heart attack, I countered. He pointed at a tiny cardboard, stapled at the end of the rope, which bore the handwritten message: Have No Fear! We used to read a lot of Green Lantern comics in those days, and having no fear was a central theme in the comics series. Had the cardboard been bigger he might have written the entire Green Lantern oath just for fun: In the brightest day, in the blackest night...

I never got to use that rope, but it eased my father's worries that I would get burned to a crisp. He loved these innovations. When my sister went to college, we were all worried that she might sleepwalk all the way to Taft Avenue from her dormitory. We were overreacting— she only had one episode of sleepwalking when she was seven. To solve this my father suggested that she tie a rope around her waist, so she could be jarred awake as she is yanked back to bed. It would have been counterproductive, especially in the event of that fire that my father had been most afraid of.

My father had a thing with ropes, fishnets, electrical wires, nails, screws, and such. We used to have a hardware store. In college when I told him that I would take the bus to pay tuition, he frantically sewed the end of a thin cord on the lining of my jeans pocket. He then tied the rolled up money with the free end of the cord. Nobody ever tried to steal the tethered wad of cash while I was sleeping inside the bus, but the university cashier stared at me impatiently as I jammed a tiny pair of scissors inside my pocket, trying to nip away at the damn cord.

My father's compulsion to fix and repair was one of the first things that faded away when the fatigue of an occult liver cancer started setting in. Instead of putting together yet another home-made extension cord, or re-reading a Legion of Superheroes comic book from the 1960's, I caught him one afternoon sitting forlornly in our hardware store, staring into space, his hands resting on his tummy. I initially assumed that he was merely getting dejected because business was doing poorly, until he started losing appetite. I had just passed the physicians' licensure exam at that time and had very little clinical experience, my proverbial "clinical eye" not yet opened wide. But when I decided to pause and really look at him, I saw what had been there all along: drooped shoulders, loose clothing, distended abdomen. Cancer, I thought. It was only a matter of locating where the tumor was and figuring out the extent. I see my parents every day, but I guess I hadn't really paid enough attention to these physical changes. It was like squinting and staring at a page of Magic Eye at a particular angle, and finally seeing a sneering unicorn hiding behind the film of fuzzy colors. I could hear my med school professors: took you long enough. When I was a medical student, I always assumed erroneously that every itch, every ache, was from cancer. I was bound to be correct at some point.

Against his token resistance we were able to drag him to the hospital for an abdominal CT scan. The results showed a liver mass that could only be a primary liver cancer. The 12-centimeter tumor, engorged and hypervascular, looked like a giant piece of prune against the bright light of the negatoscope. Its borders were irregular, its surface appearing to stretch out with its strained crevices and striations. It looked fragile, as if a tiny nick on its skin would lead to a slow egress of jelly. If only it were that innocuous, I thought miserably, if only it weren't a solid tumor with autonomy and adaptiveness. My father was not an alcoholic and never had hepatitis. Maybe he had eaten dirty peanuts contaminated with the cancer-inducing fungi aflatoxin, I told his surgeon, who was my professor from the College of Medicine. It was just the sort of inconsequential thing that a general physician who had recently studied for the medical boards would say.

The size of the mass precluded outright liver resection, and the interventional radiologist recommended something called transarterial chemoembolization (TACE). In this procedure, a wire is inserted into a blood vessel through the groin, which then delivers chemotherapy drugs directly to the liver. A tiny piece of gel is then shot up into the blood vessel, blocking the tumor's source of nutrition. It all sounded very foreign to me at the time and having talked to his attendings all I understood was that the disease was something that we would have to deal with for the rest of his life. There was only one true outcome: death. My main job was to make sure that the next few months, or years, would run as smoothly as possible. To accomplish this, I went into internal medicine residency, and eventually, medical oncology fellowship. Those decisions could be interpreted as something springing out of inspiration, a romantic sense of duty, or just a basic surge of interest in cancer, now that we have it in our own backyard. The truth was, I went into those training programs for access. Access to the facilities. Access to the right people. To clinical trials. The convenience of being able to manage everything from the ground. I knew that my father would not live long enough to see me finish fellowship and establish my own practice. Whatever service I could render him, at the time we were given, would have to be fantastic enough to compensate for it. My father was able to undergo TACE seven times, and liver surgery twice. He was one of the first to take the then-novel targeted treatment sorafenib. Liver transplantation was being considered, but by then the tumor had spread to his lungs.

The Coffin was more of a fire hazard than 611 Nakpil would ever be, and had I not enjoyed that name so much I would have probably called it The Crematorium. There were no windows in that room. It was located at the very end of a long corridor that tenants would crowd into and block in case the house burns down. My favorite feature of

The Coffin was the glossy paint on the lawanit walls that would act as fire accelerant. I had moved into The Coffin when residency training started because it was cheaper and closer to the hospital.

My father would sometimes visit me in The Coffin, no longer to conduct a fire drill, but to rest while waiting for his doctors' appointments. Not that a piece of rope would do me any good in that location, but in his prime he would have come up with something. The fatigue, anorexia, and weight loss that we first saw four years ago when he was initially diagnosed were coming back with a vengeance. Each treatment modality had been successful for a while, only for the tumor to develop resistance and the ability to evade the treatments, almost to a level of sentience. While he was sleeping in my bed, I noticed how frail he had become, his skin starting to turn yellow, blending with the mustard-colored walls of The Coffin. He would be wide awake at night and get terribly sleepy during the day. Hepatic encephalopathy, or the effects to the brain of a failing liver, was starting to set in.

At times, when he was lucid, he'd manage to fix a loose kitchen faucet, or watch an old episode of The Twilight Zone. I once played for him my favorite episode, "Nothing In The Dark", starring Robert Redford as Death. In the episode, Death tricks an old woman into letting him into her bunker, and she freaks out when she realizes who he really is. Death assures her that in dying there is "No shock. No engulfment. No tearing asunder". Maybe the lessons and perspectives of the sanctimonious Robert Redford would be strangely comforting to my father, I thought. He slept through the episode.

In those rare moments when he was awake, when he had full control of his thoughts, he would try giving advice, in his capacity as a cancer patient and as a dying parent. Never be late for your clinic, he said. Don't be one of those doctors who make patients wait for hours, only to shoo them out of the room after a rushed consult. Always be nice to them, especially the elderly. Never turn down people asking for help, even if the only motivation is to avoid potential guilt when they die. This probably explains my terrible guilt complex that borders on neurosis.

As my father's condition deteriorated further, I took an indefinite leave from fellowship and rendered bedside care at home. His kidneys were starting to shut down. As a trainee I had seen many patients with similar conditions getting stuck in the hospital. They were put through dialysis, their lungs hooked to a mechanical ventilator, never mind that the root cause of it all was a terminal disease. They would develop hospital-acquired infections, for which an infectious disease specialist would be called upon to administer multiple antibiotics and anti-fungals. They would start to fall into a coma, and a neurologist would be summoned for evaluation. Finally, they die in the ICU, surrounded by intravenous drips. My father wouldn't want that.

Still I wondered, with much dread, how he would die at home. I had hoped that it wouldn't be something visually horrific, like esophageal blood vessels bursting and causing him to vomit blood and exsanguinate. Something sudden, like a heart attack or an intracranial bleeding, would be preferable. One morning I noticed that his left calf muscle was swollen and violaceous, and I knew that it was time. Blood clots must have already formed there—only a matter of time now before they start swimming their way to his lungs. Soon enough we heard the death rattle, or the gurgling sound of saliva accumulating in the throat of someone about to die. I pronounced my father dead at 3:20 am and signed the blank death certificate I had been keeping in my desk drawer. There was a field on the blue form asking for the middle name of his mother, and in pure sleepiness I thought of asking him what it was.

When we brought his body to the funeral parlor, I remembered his dying wish not to have his face caked with make-up. The jaundice and sallowness, however, necessitated at least a thick layer of foundation. He will still look natural under the heat and brightness of the funeral lights, the mortician assured us. Come to think of it, the natural thing after dying from cancer, really, is to look ravaged, beaten, and spent. Battle scars, after putting up a good fight. But for my comfort I still opt to remember him as someone virile, someone holding on to the rope outside my apartment window, knees bent, feet planted firmly against the wall, demonstrating how to escape from a burning house with no fear. I even choose to remember him as a young kid, as he had described himself, walking in Avenida after scoring a few DC comic books sold cheap for their torn covers. For whatever alleviations selective memory might provide.

Whenever we talked about his life and his death, one of the most common comments was how lucky he was that he had lived that long for someone with liver cancer. From the dogmatic six months we were able to extend his life to five years. And it is true, as a doctor I find those five years to be miraculous. As a son, though, they were never nearly enough.

No Excuses Necessary

BRYAN EMERGES FROM THE CROWD with a pack of donuts, a pile of documents to be signed, a Coleman containing chemotherapy drugs, and a huge grin on his face. I flash a smile in return, hoping that the donuts are for me.

By now Bryan has mastered the use of prosthesis donated by a medical foundation, and his phantom leg has been getting more manageable. Whenever a patient brings up the itching and prickling of a limb that has long been amputated, I feel the urge to tell a competing story of how I used to suffer from a totally made up, self-indulgent condition called "phantom gallbladder". I've been ranting to anyone who will listen that some weird, gnawing sensation has persisted on my abdomen long after my gallbladder has been removed. I opt not to tell Bryan this story, though, because as hilarious as it is, it will no doubt initiate a conversation so drawn-out that the patients on queue will start mumbling and glaring. Bryan is a conversation black hole. I will mention in passing that I've eaten crabs in Binondo, and he will narrate a series of stories that culminates in that one time in Patpong when a lochia-soaked projectile banana hit him smack in the middle of his forehead.

The big smile is from two things: first, he has finally received the free chemotherapy drugs from PCSO after numerous tries, and second, his girlfriend Paula is accompanying him to chemotherapy today. They have been together for over 4 years now, but she has been working as a nurse in Singapore. Her vacation leave means that Bryan's mother, Aling Vicky, will have free time to go around passing medical abstracts to ask for financial assistance. Bryan has not minced words: I must prolong his life for as long as I can, enough for him to father a child and attend said child's med school graduation.

No pressure.

I will be graduating from fellowship in a few weeks, I tell him, and that the responsibility of keeping him alive will be passed on to a new fellow-in-training. He claims he will follow me in my private practice. I will be expensive, I say in jest, donuts won't cut it anymore. I imagine the tsk-tsking of all the other patients, annoyed at this cute, unnecessary chit-chat.

This is the second cycle of Bryan's new regimen of chemotherapy. We've decided to switch protocols due to the progressive worsening of the lung tumors which, if uncontrolled, will lead to respiratory failure and death. The latest chest CT scan shows that the biggest lung tumor is now the size of, dare I say it, a knee, the very origin of his cancer. In essence he now possesses a knee that has migrated to his lungs—an icebreaker he has been overusing ever since I'd described it to him in such a colorful fashion. Our goal now is to shrink this intrapulmonary knee and prevent his liver, bones, etc. from growing ectopic knees as well.

I reach for the IV needle and tie a tourniquet on his right arm. He must be getting sick of hearing this, but I mumble yet again how his dark, histrionic sleeve tattoo that crawl all the way to his hand makes putting an IV line hell. The tattoos, at least, signify that he was never afraid of needle pricks. One of his regrets when he had to get his leg lopped off was all the tattoos that went to the medical waste basket. I couldn't really make out what they were from the old photo he used to show me—I just glanced at it once with feigned interest—but there seemed to be a cactus, a Psalm, a woman, and a snake eating its own tail.

Despite the rockstar archetype that he tried to build for himself since his late teens, Bryan maintained that he has never smoked nor taken alcohol. By now we are already way past that stage where the patient bemoans getting sick despite strict adherence to guidelines of healthy living. It's like a form of passive regret, a corollary of the more spiritual "Why Me?", which is in turn a corollary of "Why Do Cunty Things Happen To Nice People". The format is familiar: I should have smoked, I should have pickled my liver with alcohol, and I should have made poor lifestyle choices if I were going to have this cancer anyway! The more well-researched patients will go even further in the checklist of factors that should have rendered this medical disaster an impossibility: I have complete vaccinations. I was never promiscuous. I have fantastic genealogy. In moments of despair, such as during bouts of retching from chemotherapy, Bryan would bring up yet again that he couldn't, for the life of him, understand why he was randomized to have an aggressive cancer.

For the most part nobody can really explain why these things happen to anybody—saintly or otherwise—but Bryan manages to console himself by blaming his occupation. He used to play in a band, but his main source of income was servicing old, broken television sets with his father, Mang Andrew. They had a repair shop somewhere in Quirino, and since high school he would accompany his father in tinkering with those old, tube-type televisions. The radiation emanating from the TV could have given him the sarcoma, he claimed, and multiple Reddit entries have affirmed him so. As soon as he recovers from the malaise and the vomiting episodes, he quickly switches back to his gregarious self, his long, belabored stories leaving no room for self-pity.

I pop in two munchkins while I prepare the charts of the other patients. Mr. Choi, a 62-year-old man with stage 4 cancer, is now on his regular follow-up check-up after completing five cycles of chemo. He seems healthy, his color is better, and his paunch seems to be making a comeback. As always, he is not accompanied by any of his relatives. He has always maintained that he doesn't need them. I've always wanted to probe further into his family story, or draw a genogram, but there was never enough time.

Mr. Choi is not an easy man to give instructions to—maybe because he is a retired professor and used to being in authority, or maybe because I don't command respect in my collarless Batman t-shirt and Crocs. On his first cycle of treatment he decided that his chemotherapy tablets were too big, so instead of taking three tablets in the morning he only took one. He was also supposed to take three tablets at night, but remorseful of the earlier underdosing, he took five tablets instead. Last month somebody donated chemotherapy intended to be given intravenously, and he decided to drink it. He was so proud narrating how he had guzzled the 10 mL vial at home that I almost crapped myself. I dashed to call The National Poison Control Center and psychiatry. He turned out okay, and his latest scan showed that the liver masses were shrinking. Obviously, I was elated that he was getting better, but I hated that this made him think that his crazy stunt worked.

I tell Mr. Choi that the next time he follows-up for chemo I will no longer be his attending physician. It's not like I expect him to get all sappy and bawl his eyes out, but I am also not prepared when he replies with:

"*Pakigawa na ako ng ten original copies ng clinical abstract bago ka umalis.*"

Well!

Lola Anna, now 80 years old, is wheeled-in by her oldest daughter. She has been my patient for almost a year now, and she has always been excited to come to the clinic. But her face is now devoid of any emotion or recognition. The cancer cachexia has gotten worse, her cheeks now hollow pits, her liver-spotted translucent skin cling-wrapped to her skeleton. Clearly the oral treatment for lung cancer is no longer working. She manages to greet me with a weak nod, and I give a polite smile in return. She refuses to eat anything, her daughter says.

All things considered it may still be considered a good run, for whatever consolation it can offer the family of a dying patient. Her diagnosis of stage 4 lung cancer came at a time when the new crop of "smart" oral cancer drugs were making their way to the local market. Gone were the days of "one-size-fits-all" chemotherapy regimens. These new molecules, called tyrosine kinase inhibitors, promised to be much more precise in seeking out previously unknown mutations. The cost of this new drug required us way more than ten copies of medical abstract, but her daughter was able to pull through. Eventually, secondary mutations rendered even these smart drugs useless. I tell them that I will be replaced by another doctor soon. This will be our last meeting, and implicitly we understand that it is not because I am graduating. I remember Lola Anna telling me that when she was initially diagnosed, she also asked herself "why me". But it wasn't a question of despair, she was quick to clarify, but a question of purpose. That there must be a purpose why she was chosen to carry this burden, a purpose that she had to discover and fulfill in the remaining moments of her life.

I finalize the patient endorsements that I'll be handing over to Jukelya Mae, the newly hired fellow-in-training. Many of these patients have been passed on to me when I first came in, patients who have survived cancer long enough to be handled by new trainees coming and going every two years. Like a teacher who won't admit to having favorites, my relationship with each patient was different. Some of them I will miss dearly, some not so much, the same way that some of these patients are more devastated than others that I am getting replaced. Regardless, I wish each of my patient success in one form or another: cure, a new drug, a clinical trial, palliation, death with dignity.

Still in an introspective mood I cross Taft to celebrate the last official day of fellowship with a huge, sugar-rich iced tea and a jaw-breaking cheeseburger. I watch the clock turn to 5 pm. I am officially done. I am overwhelmed with gratitude—to our patients who became our teachers, to our mentors in oncology who became our friends, and to our friends in The Shrine Motherfucker who became our family. There is also apprehension and regret, but the predominant feeling, strangely, is sadness.

My phone rings. It's Gina Silva, a batchmate from high school. It is one of those calls.

"Hi! Are you still in fellowship? Can I ask for a favor? My boyfriend's sister needs an MRI for a knee injury, do you think you can help her get in, as a charity patient *ha*?"

This time, though, I do not need to scamper for an explanation on why I don't have a special power in this hospital. I do not need to give an excuse. I do not need to lie and feel guilty.

"Hi Gina, sorry I'm officially no longer affiliated with the hospital! Let me give you the trunkline to call! How's Frankie?"

I was wrong. The predominant feeling is not sadness, but relief.

TIME TO WORK

Private Practice Marketing Primer

WE KNEW, PLUMMETING HEADFIRST into private practice, that nobody would be tripping all over themselves to refer their patients to us, but we never realized how difficult it was just to make people know that we exist. Passing the oncology subspecialty boards was not, in any way, something that could be parlayed into a spectacular real-world debut. That year, only eight of us had taken the exam over two quiet weekends, and there was no social media fanfare. This was in contrast to passing the Physicians' Licensure Exam, which was a surefire way to have your face printed on a politician-sponsored tarpaulin, displayed in the town plaza for everyone to ignore.

When the thrill of passing the oncology boards had died down, along with the self-indulgent reflections on the rigors of medical training, what was left was a dreadful realization: it's time to work. But there was no work. Still, I only had to look at the trajectory of Thymes' career to resist the urge to swipe my face with a razor blade.

Enter my mother, who had not toiled for over a decade just to hear her aging son whine, read comic books, and ruminate over fancy concepts like ennui and weltschmerz. She wasn't the type to nag me into snapping out of post-fellowship faux-drama, so one morning she got hold of my box of business cards and started handing them out to any random person she met. She had excellent marketing skills, which involved going to the wet market daily to buy pork and chicken, while disseminating my business cards around. She was, essentially, one step away from being an official "promodizer", if only she knew how to print bigger, glossier promotional materials.

On one such trip to the market she noted that the face of Aling Poquita, her high school classmate, was swollen. "*Poquita, bakit ka manas?*" she asked with genuine care and affection. My mother had developed a clinical eye herself, and she knew that facial edema was indicative of something very serious.

"*Kahapon lang yan, naghahanap nga ako ng doctor,*" Aling Poquita said. "*Parang hirap na rin ako huminga.*"

"*Teka, may dala yata akong card ng anak ko...*"

Before I knew it random people she had chatted in the wet market, or in the lines in Bayad Center, were coming to our house for consults. I told my mom that solicitation is unethical, but she insisted that she was only trying to help her friends and neighbors in the barangay. Her approach, of course, did not always get the desired effect.

"*Ano ang ibig sabihin ng oncologist?*" an elderly man asked as he pored through the card that my mother had handed him.

"*Doctor sa cancer!*" she replied merrily, which made the man fling the card back in panic. The card could have very well borne the message: You are invited to come and have cancer.

For those who could muster enough interest, they would ask where my clinic was located. My mom would point to our house. My "business card" was missing the most important details after all: clinic hours and location. The cards, given as a gift by a friend, only had my name, title, and a telephone number. I was still in the process of looking for hospitals where I could hold my clinics, as the practice of putting up a clinic at home was already deemed obsolete. The plan to convert our hardware store into a clinic, a quaint idea that might have worked in the 90's, had been scrapped long ago.

Our hardware store, located beside the garage, had been showing signs of dying in the past few years. When my father died, we decided to sell whatever merchandise was left and officially close shop. One of the products left to consume was *sahing*, a kind of resin being used for industrial purposes. This stuff was also widely used by *albularyos'* for its inherent heat and supposed healing properties. The albularyos would write prayers and incantations on tiny pieces of paper and, using sahing as adhesive, vigorously slap them on the patients' ailing body parts. Eventually people in really depressed areas who couldn't afford the "donations" for albularyos would self-medicate with sahing. In many instances people would buy *sahing* from my mom, and she would ask, "*San mo gagamitin?*" The conversation would lead into a long story about a tumor palpated over the inguinal area, or an aching knee, or a black spot on the sole of the left foot which had started to swell and bleed.

"*Hindi gamot ang sahing,*" my mom would start. "*Alam mo, may anak akong doktor.*"

The latest extreme marketing stunt happened back in March when I was delivering a speech to elementary school graduates as a guest speaker. As with most newly minted medical specialists I had been summoned by my alma mater to come up with something inspiring.

It was tempting to say "Medicine is not as glamorous as you think! Also, I'm still poor!", but I was afraid I would get booed and hissed at by the parents. Trying to be cool and progressive during speeches was no longer cool and progressive anyway, so I just gave a generic five-minute speech, smiled, and left. When I got home, carrying my plaque of appreciation, various St. Magdalene of Canossa merchandise, and a small bag of groceries, my mom said that my speech had gotten her all misty. She had, apparently, dragged my aunt to the school, and they watched the darn thing in secret. I was amused at first, but I suddenly suspected that something strange must have happened. I frantically asked her to show me my box of calling cards. It was almost empty, and I cringed as I realized what happened.

Beaming with pride at her own marketing zest, my mother finally admitted that while I was delivering my speech, she was slowly going around the audience area, distributing my calling cards. "*Anak ko yan,*" she whispered as she jostled through the crowd. She claimed that the parents were delighted to receive the cards, and that she had received many compliments for having raised such an inspiring young man.

The Illusion of Mixturization

SEVEN MONTHS AFTER we had enthusiastically submitted our application forms and paid a hefty amount for gym memberships, Dan, Hatchett, and I decided to actually work-out. We were getting deconditioned, atherosclerotic, and dyspneic at rest, and we knew that there was no escaping this basic requirement for health called "moving". So, after gorging on chicken fingers, french fries, fried mushroom, and iced tea, the three of us hauled our untoned asses to the gym. We even hired a personal trainer, Coach Marcus de Sade, who would hold us accountable and oversee our journey to temporary hotness. I mean health—we were totally there for health reasons.

Our excuses for not working out were long and varied: we were busy trying to jumpstart our practice, the hot people were making us feel insecure, the bathroom floor could be caked with coagulated semen, and so on. We also argued that regularly running on the treadmill would cause facial sagging, necessitating the premature use of facial thread lifts and fillers. And don't even start on the proliferation of wrinkles from all the straining that comes with deadlifts. Hatchett, a pediatrician, was already working full time as a vaccine trialist. Her husband, Dan, was just starting his private practice as a nephrologist. They also had to focus on making a baby. All valid and sane reasons.

But my favorite reason of all was that I was convinced I was terminally ill. Again. It had become a habit. An annual event. This time it was rectal cancer. I was so sure—so sure this time—that a huge solid mass was expanding within my rectum and lifting weights just to be fit would therefore be pointless. I would soon be confined to a bed, feeding through a tube, and no detailed computation of macros and a gazillion reps of bosu squats could prevent that. Granted I had seen so many colorectal cancer patients that particular week, and the residents' Grand Rounds was about rectal cancer in the young, but I was also starting to develop things you couldn't just invent or attribute to paranoia, like actual signs and symptoms. And it doesn't matter if you're a doctor or not, the first thing you do if you suspect that you have cancer is to check Google and plummet into a blackhole of despair. I was able to find one article that says decreased caliber of stools is not necessarily associated with gastrointestinal cancers, that it's a fallacy that had gone unchecked through the many editions of internal medicine textbooks. So at least there was that, but then I started to bleed.

As I was kneeling in front of the toilet bowl dissecting my own bloody feces with barbecue sticks in my hands and a penlight in my mouth, I knew that instead of planking and bear crawling I would rather spend the remaining days of my life going through all the seven deadly sins. Kneeling in front of the bowl wasn't just for melodrama. I had to investigate if fresh blood had dripped into the bowl, or if the blood had been pre-processed and admixed with the chunky substance of the stool. They say that admixed blood may indicate a tumor. But what if the blood, say from a lowly hemorrhoid, had dripped into the bowl then seeped through the fecal crevices, creating the illusion of mixturization? That the blood wasn't necessarily blenderized with pre-fecal materials intraluminally? For sure there's a Google article, or an entire video, on that. But what if it wasn't blood after all, but undigested bright red chili?

Maybe I should get a specimen for fecalysis, I thought, in a moment of lucidity. But what if I miss the portion that has actual blood? I remember asking a patient once if he had already submitted his stool sample in the laboratory. He said that the sample was still in his bag and would I want to see it. Before I could insist that it wouldn't be necessary, he unzipped his Jansport backpack and brought out a huge mayonnaise jar containing a girthy, seven-inch turd, like one of those formalinized sea cucumbers in the National Museum. I guess he didn't want to miss a spot during sampling.

It was my gastroenterologist friend, Aries, who disproved my assertion that I was dying. He did that by happily shoving a scope up my ass.

"I want to be awake when you probe me!" I told Aries. "I want to see the tumor that has unceremoniously, uninvitedly, uncouthly entered my life, when all this time I have been nothing but a good son, a kind friend, a caring physician, with a special interest in the field of epidemiology..."

"All right, all right we won't put you to sleep. Geez, the drama," Aries said as he slathered the scope with jelly.

Having ruled out any sort of tumor, I knew, to be perfectly frank, that I was granted a new lease in life, a second chance to correct my mistakes, a bright new day, bla bla bla no more excuses not to exercise. Coach Marcus De Sade was already waiting in the gym doing bicep curls. Dan and Hatchett were already getting ripped. While I was celebrating The 8th Annual Feast of Hypochondria they had been feverishly mastering all sorts of kettlebells and cable exercises.

Coach Marcus proved to be a patient trooper. He asked me for my fitness goals, and I narrated a drawn-out story that was definitely meant as a delaying tactic. I confessed that I'd discovered how out of shape I was during internship when I checked on a patient during monitoring duty and discovered that he was dead. There was no one else in sight, so I yelled "code!" as loud as I could and started the chest compressions by myself. I compressed the chest one, two, three, and after the third compression, I was panting. I was out of breath, making an otherworldly wheezing-yelping-whining cacophony as I gasped for air. Luckily someone barged in to save me from this embarrassment (an insensitive thought, when what I should have been thankful for was someone had barged in to save the patient from death). We were once taught in basic and advanced cardiac life support training that some of the reasons to stop resuscitating include: if the patient is brain dead, if there are signs of lividity, and notably, if the one doing the chest compressions is exhausted. I didn't want anybody dying during CPR just because I was an unhealthy loser, so I enrolled in the new gym that had just been constructed near our house.

On my first day in the "*bakal*" gym I used the treadmill for 30 minutes, lifted a couple of weights, struggled with the rowing machine, became totally dizzy, ran to the bathroom, and hurled. I then resumed my work-out. The instructor must have noted how anxious I looked as I lifted the tiniest dumb bells with my wobbly forearms, so he approached me, touched my shoulder, and said, "*Hijo, kaya mo yan.*" And then some huge, muscular guy asked me to spot him. I didn't know what spotting meant, the word "spotting" instantly triggering thoughts of imminent abortion or cervical neoplasia. I said sure, and when I realized what I had to do I suddenly became afraid—for him. If he got crushed under those huge metallic thingies it would take me hours to dislodge them from his crushed sternum. I was able to frequent that gym for two months, and I remember making the vow that those two months of exercise should be good enough for five years.

Coach Marcus waved my self-deprecating stories away and said that every day in the gym is a gift from God. He was inspiring and wonderful, except when he was preoccupied with grossly unrelated stuff. He looked particularly distracted one lazy afternoon, and I heard that he was going through some girlfriend issues. While I was planking and sweating horrendously, thinking good thoughts to distract myself from the pain, looking all sorts of stupid with my elbows perched on a giant pink ball, Coach Marcus asked, in all earnestness:

"*Doc, ano ang mas importante, isip o puso?*"

In response I think I've mumbled, "*daiflkdlfsa?*"

It wasn't gibberish. It was totally a combination of "this is not the time", "my abdominal muscles are very painful", and "introspection is the killer of the soul".

Alone/Alone

THE LIT-UP BILLBOARDS shifting in rhythm to the tune of a strangely cheerful dirge announced that I was finally in New York City. I had just been dropped off at The Row NYC Hotel by my service driver, Mr. Mongkut, a gregarious, elderly man who had enumerated the pre-school exploits of his grandchildren throughout our ride from JFK. It was reportedly colder than usual, but at 9 pm I decided to take a leisurely walk along Times Square, going through all the tourist traps my friends had warned me about. Going against the most common advice, I snapped a photo of the frolicking sidewalk mascots wearing bootleg costumes, surreptitiously lest I get harassed for tips. I walked into a sex shop with its walls of Betamax cassettes and dildoes, the yellowing clam shell packaging indicating that they were remnants of the San Fernando Valley porn boom in the '80's. I paid too much for Reese's in a glittery container that is now sitting with the rest of the clutter. My attitude towards tourist traps is one of ambivalence. You feel like a total idiot falling for them, but you at least get whiny stories that you can tell your friends back home.

It was my first time in New York. I was to attend an annual oncology convention with another oncologist, Dr. Cholo, but a few days before the flight he had suffered a stroke. There was a superstitious belief among medical professionals that a few days before a trip, a strange series of events would attempt to stop you from leaving. You might get sick, or your patients might start getting sicker. You could try to escape Manila, but not without emotional baggage. And certainly not without guilt. A day before my Copenhagen trip in 2016 a patient developed severe allergic reactions from chemotherapy and had to be intubated. The last text message I received before boarding a plane to Tokyo in the summer of 2017 was of a patient's daughter, reporting that her father with brain cancer was having seizures. On both occasions, and in all other similar circumstances, I was able to hand over the cases to physicians who were kind enough to cover for me. Still, I would catch myself catastrophizing, imagining that my patients would start dropping like flies, when I should be listening to the tour guide regaling us with tales of The Little Mermaid, or explaining the history of the Snoopy Museum. Such frivolities, when you are needed back here, I imagined my patients scolding me. A week before the flight I had already started writing down all my patient endorsements, filling up their Philhealth and PCSO forms, ringing up the doctors who would receive them. It was like a rehearsal in putting together a last will and testament, all for a five-day conference in New York.

Everything's Gonna be Fine. Fine. Fine—the marquee of *Jagged Little Pill: The Musical* on top of the Broadhurst Theater screamed. If anything, I was hoping that it would be a good prognostication of how this very short trip would be. I wasn't really into musicals, but Jagged Little Pill was the soundtrack of my generation. Even if none of us had ever fellated anybody in a theater, we would scream a guttural "You Oughta Know" to the horror of the Canossian sisters back in '96.

Nobody cared if none of the situations Alanis Morissette was rattling off were actually ironic, "Ironic" was our high school anthem, and saying "chardonnay" made us feel extremely sophisticated.

At the back exit of the adjacent Shubert Theater, I heard a small group of fans clapping and giggling, as performers of Aaron Sorkin's adaptation of *To Kill A Mockingbird* exited the theater one by one. I waved to Ed Harris, screaming "Ed! Ed! I loved you in *The Hours!* Ed!", and imagined that he waved back. In truth a bouncer blocked our view and sneered menacingly. I went theater hopping in search of more *artista*, but no such luck. It was the equivalent of my mother prowling the *sosyal* malls like Powerplant, just in case a local celebrity was shopping there on a weekend.

By the fifth theater hop, the latté I had bought on the way out of the hotel was getting cold. I did not even feel like having coffee, but in the movies people in Manhattan always seem to be rushing along the sidewalks, evading metal scaffoldings and other pedestrians, a paper cup of boiling coffee clasped in each hand. And for a few days I thought that maybe I could take on that image, of someone perpetually rushing but still contemplative, pretending that my soul was being weighed down by some sort of crisis, imagining that someone was recording me on film. Some spiritual or philosophical crisis, perhaps, which would be more dramatic than being conscience-stricken over what could be happening to my patients in my absence. And to complete this pretense, what should be running through my mind as I was hurtling through the streets: the fantastic short story—

no, novel—that I would soon be writing. It would be a modern-day romance, or a murder mystery. Or, what the heck, a bildungsroman.

A violent blast of wind promptly snapped me out of this solitary melodrama. All of a sudden, the weather was no longer conducive to any sort of introspection. It was reportedly 49 degrees, aggravated by a bit of drizzle. I started walking back to the hotel. As I turned on my phone's LTE to access Google Maps, all the Viber messages came flooding in. Patient Sonia P, a 70-year-old woman newly diagnosed with lung cancer, had sent her bone scan results showing multiple spread to the bones. She was distraught, her back was aching, and she needed to talk to me ASAP. In came another message from a nurse, asking where I had left the morphine prescription for patient Hallicurd Allivo. I forgot to leave one. Miriam P., a patient with rectal cancer, said that she was having severe diarrhea from the radiation. A few other similar messages came rushing in.

Whenever I'm in another country I allow myself the pleasure of smoking one cigarette. There, in a dark corner on West 44 street and 11th Avenue, with the NYPD sirens blaring in the background, and hot steam puffing up from manholes, I decided to have my New York cigarette. Across the street, a woman was rummaging through the trash. A vagrant approached me, asking for a cigarette. His hands were trembling, maybe from the cold, maybe from alcohol withdrawal. I gave him one and hurriedly walked away.

I had gotten quite used to the breakfast buffets offered in hotels and assumed that the "breakfast voucher" provided by The Row NYC Hotel would be enough to sustain me until dinnertime.

"Ya get one choice of fruit, one choice of drink, and one choice of cereal!" Vito, the big, muscular guy behind the cafeteria counter barked. Having consumed my fill of New York *lakatan* and Kellogg's cereals I crossed the street to the convention center at Marriott Marquis. Being surrounded by medical specialists from all over the world never fails to heighten my Impostor Syndrome. I eavesdropped on two very tall oncologists as they were feasting on apple and hot tea, and discovered that they were discussing the results of the clinical trial on pembrolizumab, the latest darling drug for non-small cell lung adenocarcinoma. I had no intention of joining the discussion, but I was eyeing that huge bowl on the registration desk containing an assortment of imported chocolate bars. I stashed a handful in my bag. Noticing my embarrassment, Ashley, the receptionist, said I could get more, adding that she had lots more in the drawer.

"I've been trying to dispose of them!" she admitted. I would be snacking on free Reese's throughout this trip, I thought, content that I have, so far, behaved like a stereotypical Pinoy tourist. After listening to a few lectures on the latest chemotherapy updates I decided to escape.

My route to The Metropolitan Museum of Art took me through Central Park. I gave in to the temptation to sit on one of the benches to compose a few paragraphs of pretentious prose, with Tom Waits wailing on my music player. The joggers and families having a picnic were a fascinating distraction, and I ended up starting a horrendous story about an alcoholic doctor being stalked by a cancer patient's daughter. It was crap, but it was crap written in Manhattan, and I was wearing a gray newsboy cap, a pair of dark blue earmuffs, and having spiked cappuccino while writing it. After one page of corny, lazy prose I ended up taking photographs of inanimate objects— rows of maple trees, the huge schist rocks, the bushes, the pond. In other words, strategic spots where murder victims in *Law and Order: Special Victims Unit* are frequently discovered.

My friend Abby Chan, who is now based in South Carolina, had told me that there was no way I could go through all the works in The Metropolitan Museum of Art in a few hours, and that I should just zoom in on a particular field of interest. After having myself photographed on the concrete steps with the scarlet signage of "The Met" in full view, I went straight to the Temple of Dendur in the Egyptian wing. Abby's kids love Egyptian history, and as my sense of wonder had been eroded over time by my own neglect and the demands of work, I decided to follow their recommendation. Most of the relics in the vast Egyptian wing were about royalty and death, each piece a mixture of the beautiful and the frightening. The predominantly gold and black motif of the sarcophagi and the sphinxes gave them a kind of deceptive grandeur, which lasted for a few minutes, to be supplanted immediately by claustrophobia and dread. Many times, during my walk through the relics, I had to inhale sharply from the anxiety of getting trapped, as well as from allergic rhinitis.

On my long walk back to the hotel I thought that it was time to take a video of myself quoting a popular New York character from literature or cinema. Maybe something morose and painful by Joe Kavalier from Michael Chabon's *The Amazing Adventures of Kavalier and Clay*, or something menacing from Matt Murdock, aka *Daredevil*. I couldn't remember any of their lines at that moment, but I had just seen *Alone/Together*. I turned the camera on myself, and for ten seconds I was Liza Soberano pleading to his manipulative boyfriend, "But hon, I want to see The Met! I want to see The Met!"

My friend Melinda, who had been working as a nurse in Long Island for over 20 years, offered to take me around the city. Upon learning of my New York visit, many friends had reached out, but nothing could be more concrete and enticing than "I have a car and I will pick you up from your hotel in five minutes!" The three layers of heat tech that made me tolerate a few seconds of cold in the pavement now made me feel like I was in a sarcophagus inside Melinda's SUV. Jet lag was kicking in, and as I was trying to fight off nausea, I weakly told her some courtesy gossip about our high school friends. I couldn't get too fake-animated in telling my stories, though, as it might prompt me to hurl my breakfast of fruit, drink, and choice of cereal on her dashboard. Our trip to the Holy Grail of all US destinations—the outlet shops—would take 54 minutes, according to her GPS screen. I closed my eyes in an attempt to hold my breakfast in. As I was about to doze off, I was snapped back into consciousness by the squalling of a baby.

"What's going on there, honey? You dropped your toy again?" Melinda said as she took a sharp turn. George, her youngest, was apparently sleeping in a baby seat at the back the entire time. "Will, please be a dear and try to reach for his toy on the floor?" she asked. "But I might flood the floor with vomitus" didn't sound like a good reason, so I turned around and blindly groped for things on the corrugated rubber floor, grabbing an apple, a half-eaten piece of bread, and a bottle of milk in the process. George squealed as I finally handed him the Elmo plush toy.

Melinda had come to the US a year after 9-11 with an undergraduate degree in Communications. Eventually she found herself taking up Nursing, did very well, and is now the chief surgical nurse in a major hospital. She had completely transformed from a meek, soft-spoken girl back in high school, into someone who does not take crap from anyone. "I can't be *mahinhin* here, or the ego of those surgeons will eat me alive." At the outlet stores my lack of retail skills was solved by letting Melinda do the pasalubong shopping for me. I pushed George's stroller in return.

During our Mexican fast food lunch, she noted that I was constantly apologizing for being on my phone. I explained that I'd been answering the queries of my patients, such as Sonya P, who'd tried the steroid prescription I had sent via Viber but was now experiencing abdominal pains. I confessed that these messages feel like huge hands choking me. I could be in Madrid or Chicago or Greenhills, and they would still reach out to claw at me. And if I ignored them, I would choke on my own guilt.

"You know what your problem is, you're too accessible! That ain't gonna happen here!" she glowered. I explained that I'd tried filtering these messages through a secretary, through my residents, or through a teleconsultation platform, but they proved to be inefficient.

"You have to draw the line somewhere, or you'll go bonkers. You need someone you can trust. Train someone if you need to. That is not selfishness, that's self-preservation. You know who protects my doctors from this sort of insanity? Me. You need someone to teach you how to do it? Well allow me." I suddenly had a personal shopper, tour guide, and life coach all at the same time. I tried to recall if I'd been nice to her back in high school, in order to guilt myself if I wasn't. I think I was.

I was finally able to watch *Jagged Little Pill: The Musical*, where everyone enjoyed wailing vitriolic songs of heartbreak and angst. My seatmate was particularly rowdy, and I had to giggle like a superior jerk every time she got the lyrics wrong. Realizing that musicals were something I could be enjoying after all, I went straight into another musical, Wicked, at The Gershwin Theater. Bad idea. By this time jetlag was too strong to overcome, and after the fantastic Defying Gravity performance, with Elphaba getting hoisted up in the air and all, I fell asleep all the way to the curtain call. Alcoholic drinks were available in the lobby, there was that, and after getting myself sufficiently smashed I teetered out of the theater.

For my final night in the city, I decided to just walk where my exhausted feet would take me. Trying to conquer the requisite tourist destinations was futile in five days, and my aimless strolling took me to The Grand Central Station, home to many kidnappings, murders, and explosions in books and movies. But the first time I'd read about it was in *The Catcher In The Rye*, when Holden slept on one of its benches.

I grabbed a slice of pizza at the Dining Concourse and cracked open the Wonder Woman trade paperback I had purchased at Midtown Comics. At the table across from me a man was reading a hardcover Mary Higgins Clark, a huge set of earphones on his head. At another table, three men were playing a board game that looked like Cluedo. I felt like I'd just walked into a 90's pocket of time located in a chronal train station. To go with the theme, I plugged in my earphones and played 10,000 Maniacs.

I stared up at the artificial stars dotting the celestial ceiling, ice cream cone in my hand, and felt a gnawing sensation in my stomach. The realization that my long trek back to Manila would be commencing in a few hours had fully dawned on me, and it made me want to retch. I had prepared for this very brief trip for months, happily saying goodbye to my patients, only for technology to make a full escape impossible. My brief role play as a world-weary writer with some vague crisis-of-sorts, or a theater aficionado, or Liza, would soon come to an end, to be replaced by the very real role of a prematurely burned-out physician tending to the crises of others. I never liked to admit that the job was exhausting, not because it would reveal vulnerability, but because I hated the implication that I was trying to feel self-important. Fatigue had become a form of self-indulgence. This trip was in no way relaxing, there were no big revelatory moments about myself, no profound epiphanies, no...

A blast of freezing wind hit me in the face as I walked out of the Grand Central Station, and the melodramatics had to pause. There were seven blocks to traverse to get back to my hotel. I put my newsboy cap back on, turned my music player up to maximum volume, and got myself a warm cup of coffee to keep me company through my brisk walk. One final performance, so to speak.

Afternoon Tea

IN THE MIDDLE OF ENJOYING afternoon tea like a *tita-in-training* I managed to eavesdrop on a bevy of bonafide *titas* sitting at the next table. I usually feel a twinge of guilt whenever I strain to eavesdrop, but this time no effort was necessary. The three titas were all screaming, as if in a performance. It was a fascinating one-act play, and I was there for it. Private practice can sometimes make one feel isolated, and you have to find thrills wherever you can.

The one-act play commenced with a prolonged confrontation with the manager. Tita Karen complained that she was given full cream milk on the side, instead of non-fat milk. The manager insisted that it was non-fat milk. But it tastes so rich! Tita Karen protested. Maybe you have accidentally swapped each others' vials of milk, the valiant manager tried to explain, unperturbed by the strong tita energy. The titas started drinking from all the mugs, smacking their tongues to evaluate the richness, the silkiness, the molecular properties of the different kinds of milk.

Having resolved this issue Tita Annabelle proceeded to complain about the insurance she had just paid for her Subaru.

"But how about the insurance for your Volkswagen? The Fortuner? The Lexus?" Tita Franny asked.

"*Yeah I paid for them na rin, mahal ha!*" Tita Annabelle said with a pout. I had a sinking suspicion from then on that Tita Franny was like the B-lister playing the supportive best friend role in the group.

Tita Karen then discussed the geo-politics of expensive bags. She was once traveling in Jerusalem, when she noticed that the luggage of another tita, Tita Tita, was LV. This made Tita Karen feel deeply embarrassed, because while she was also carrying an LV, it was only a tiny purse!

"*Nahiya talaga ako*," she said. "*Pero at least hindi naman ako naka Lacoste, noh! Ha ha ha!*" Lacoste, she explained, is "something you just give away to your maids".

"I would rather carry around a generic, brand-less bag, than carry Lacoste! *Ano ako, nouveau riche*? At least if someone points out that your bag is generic, your excuse is that you like the style! Ha ha ha!"

Like the two guys snickering at the other table, I was also having boatloads of fun listening in. But then they started talking about whose total hysterectomy was more painful, as well as the rejuvenating benefits of rubbing fresh placenta on your face, so I concluded that it was time to leave.

The Mansion

FOR A MOMENT Smoketh actually believed that their intense, heart-to-heart talk with their father worked. Yesterday she sat him in the middle of the room, and told him how his uncontrollable urge to hoard paintings, ancient Kenyan pottery, and nubile teenyboppers was wreaking havoc in their lives. Her older sister, Mabel, a palliative care doctor, had switched on her soothing doctorly voice, as if she really believed that this was a problem that could only end in death. For years they would deal with Mr. Yap's eccentricities by name-dropping their dearly departed mother, shoving a Powerpoint presentation of their finances to his face, or sprinkling mood stabilizers on his herbal tea. Nothing ever worked. This time, Mabel talked to him the way she talked to a terminally ill patient—with genuine love and care but with enough art to inquire if he wanted to sign a do-not-resuscitate status while his head was clear.

After the focused group intervention Smoketh and Mabel were thrilled. Talking to a family member, with gentleness and love, actually worked!

For a few hours.

The following day, they watched in absolute terror as delivery men hauled in a life-size replica of the Black Nazarene. Any hope that his hoarding addiction had diminished was quickly destroyed, as they watched Mr. Yap clapping and jumping while the statue was being polished.

"This is the real Black Nazarene," he said. "The real one!"

Smoketh stared across the empty swimming pool and waved at Mabel who was sitting dejectedly in the cottage, her face contorted in a mixture of resigned infuriation and learned helplessness. Almost in synchrony they blew cigarette smoke in the air. Mabel then flicked the cigarette butt into the biggest ashtray of all—the empty swimming pool. Smoketh sneered at the absurdity of that huge, mildewed cavity sitting miserably in the middle of the garden. It had been years since anybody had used such an impractical vortex of water and electricity.

When they were kids their classmates from Maryknoll would gush at how fortunate they were for living in a mansion with a pool. After swimming with Melanie and Pia, they would run to the kitchen, lured by the smell of cinnamon and boiling hot chocolate. They would leave behind trails of water on the parquet floor, promptly wiped dry by their *manangs*. Their mother, Blessilda, would serve bread on expensive plates. She was not a huge fan of saving the most precious china for special occasions, or wrapping the sofa in plastic, for that matter.

Smoketh was starting to get worried for her career. She should be concentrating on establishing her practice as a medical specialist by now. She should be plotting how to infiltrate all the hospitals in the city. Instead, she was losing her mind trying to get rid of expensive junk without eliciting mass hysteria. She was, in fact, one bonsai delivery away from luring her dad into a vacation in Hongkong, just so she could freely have an open house for anyone to just grab anything. I suggested that we throw everything into the pool and dump huge amounts of cement in it. Smoketh sneered at the ridiculousness of the suggestion, because she would need ten empty pools to accommodate everything.

"The things that you see here—all these swords, the jewelries, the Black Nazarene. All of these, except for the bonsai, I will pass on to you and your sister when I die."

"Dad, I would like to make it clear, that we are not interested in owning any of these stuff," Smoketh said. "But just out of curiosity, why not give us the bonsai as well?"

"The bonsai goes to Marjorie."

"Who the heck is Marjorie," she asked, but in the pit of her stomach she already knew.

"Marjorie is the niece of our driver Fred," he smiled. "She's very pretty. I already booked a ticket for her flight from Sultan Kudarat."

"Well, you know what," Smoketh yelled. "I love bonsai! Yes, dad, give me the bonsai. Give me everything!"

Smoketh drove through afternoon QC traffic accompanied by ten pots of bonsai sitting like expensive, moldy turd on the backseat. Mr. Yap had called her bluff and happily gave her some samplers. These beauties would, supposedly, give her an appreciation of horticulture, and allow her to reevaluate her feelings for it. She had one feeling for it, and it needed no re-evaluation: hate.

"Hi doc," Noemie, her secretary, said cheerily. Smoketh flashed a half-smile and handed her a small pot. That's your problem now!

"OMG do I finally have patients?" she whispered, noting the flock of people impatiently watching afternoon soap in the waiting area. For months Smoketh would come to this clinic, sit for two hours, and wait. And wait some more. And go home with absolutely no income. After weeks of having zero patients and the clinic bills started coming in, she had decided to turn off the airconditioning. Then some of the lights. She was also able to go through all the Narnia novels. Next stop: The Brothers Karamazov!

"*Patients po sila nung derma,*" Noemie said, pointing to the adjacent clinic.

Smoketh turned on her Mac. If anything, these patient-less clinic hours had given her some time to work on the accounting of the household expenses. Last month, her father's purchase of ancient books amounted to two hundred thousand pesos. Collection of antique weaponry: three hundred thousand pesos. Paintings: five hundred thousand. Their walls were now plastered with paintings that had no common theme. Most were not even mounted up, just stacked on the floor, waiting for a queen termite or an accidental ember from Ate Mabel's cigarettes to save them from their gratuitous existence.

Mr. Yap's obsession for accumulating things started when he retired from his professorial job in the university. At that time their chain of appliance stores had started to pick up, and money came rolling in. He also invested in multi-level marketing and became quite masterful at it. That was the time when various renovation jobs started on their old bungalow, constructions giving birth to more and more extensions, additional floors, a swimming pool, an annex A and an annex B, until the house had transmogrified into a patchwork mansion both quaint and garish. Rooms, attics, dens that served no practical purpose started to appear, and why anyone would want a goddamn fireplace in Quezon City was anybody's guess.

His collecting hobby started with paintings. The first was a bootleg version of Johannes Vermeer's Girl With a Pearl Earring, which he had probably purchased for ten times it's worth. He bought it to impress the seller, Minda Villanueva, whom Smoketh had suspected was his mistress. Word got around among sellers that there was this millionaire who was both lecherous and gullible, i.e., the perfect client for things nobody would ever need. If the seller was some mildly attractive female and could feign giggles at his off-color jokes, he would pay huge amounts of money for a framed poster of Fido Dido from Expressions.

Noemie knocked on the cubicle door. Smoketh braced herself for her first and possibly only patient for the day.

"Hi doc!" It was Charles, a medical representative, deflating any hope for at least one patient for today.

With a shrill Mabel woke Smoketh up on a Sunday. While downing his herbal concoction for breakfast, Mr. Yap suddenly fell face down on the quartz countertop and dropped on the floor. In the hurly burly of things Mabel had forgotten that she was, in fact, a doctor and automatically assumed that Mr. Yap was dead. Smoketh hurtled to the kitchen and immediately noted, upon hearing him groan, that he was very much alive.

"No hospitals! No hospitals! No hospitals!" Mr. Yap chanted

"Let's go the hospital! Call Fred we'll bring the Fortuner!" Smoketh yelled.

"The driver's not here. He's in the airport to pick up his niece!"

Smoketh decided to drive the SUV herself. "Just make sure he's still breathing," she instructed Mabel, who was slowly rolling down the car window so she could smoke this anxiety away. Smoketh glared at her on the rearview mirror.

For a Sunday, the emergency room was packed. Smoketh asked the resident doctor if she could insert the intravenous line herself, since all the nurses were busy. She also wanted to spare any personnel from having to deal with this very irascible man. Mr. Yap had been throwing invectives non-stop, his curses getting more and more slurred by the minute. Let's just wait for the utility worker to bring Sir Ramon to the CT scan department, the resident doctor stammered. "I'll do it!" Smoketh proclaimed, and in two seconds she was whizzing through the corridors with the stretcher.

"Lacunar infarcts," Smoketh told the only available personnel in the ER—an intern—who was nodding her head, more out of courtesy than academic interest. Smoketh predicted that the blinking lights and the rhythmic beeps in the Stroke Unit would drive her father insane. He would then drive everyone else insane, screaming that his bed sheet needs to be replaced or that his IV is not running properly. Smoketh would then have to go on a daily apology tour.

A hemorrhagic conversion, brain surgery, and one bout of hospital-acquired pneumonia later, Mr. Yap was ready for discharge. He did not have insurance. His credit cards were all maxed out. Smoketh managed to work out a scheme with the financial counselor that would essentially have her guaranteeing the payments after discharge.

"Unless I get a subarachnoid hemorrhage first, because I don't even have a practice to speak of!" Smoketh later told me while we were eating microwaved dinner in the nearby convenience store. I did not want to sound facetious, but it was such a low-hanging fruit that needed to be said: Maybe they will accept the Black Nazarene as payment!

"I wish," Smoketh said as she furiously shoved microwaved adobo in her mouth. "Or bronze weapons, cannons, sofas, bootleg Botong Francisco's, bootleg Rolexes…"

What a shock it must have been for waifish, young Miss Marjorie to travel all the way from Sultan Kudarat, expecting to take on the role of the exotic romantic interest of a business magnate, only to be welcomed by someone requiring tube feeding and bedpans. Instead of the shopping spree that Uncle Fred had promised her, she found herself giving baths to a curmudgeon in a leaking bathtub that nobody had used in decades. To her credit she was the only one who could coax Mr. Yap into taking his cholesterol medications, all the private nurses having given up after a few weeks of verbal abuse.

When Marjorie first came in Mabel and Smoketh took it upon themselves to tour her around. To someone who had spent her whole life in a hovel, the expanse of the mansion itself must have seemed threatening. This is the master's bedroom, where he and my mother used to sleep, Smoketh pointed out. In their place, hundreds of matryoshka dolls from Estonia and from online shopping were sprawled like massacre victims. Behind another arthritic door: more ancient weapons. They guided her through the corridors, walking around mystical anitos, vases that must have nested all sorts of tiny animals, glass-framed commemorative bank notes that were probably given away by banks so they could de-clutter. And of course, the Black Nazarene, which was now bald as the wig was undergoing re-styling, as per Mr. Yap's request.

In the library Marjorie's eyes widened at the rows of Encyclopedia Americana, Collier's Encyclopedia, and hardcover volumes of Reader's Digest Condensed Books. Marjorie attempted to make small talk by gushing at how expensive these old books must be by now, to which Mabel replied, with unintentional harshness, "A *magbobote* will give probably give us fifty pesos for everything, depending on the total weight". They made their way to Annex B, leading her to a room that contained the mansion's centerpiece.

The doors swung open, revealing a high-ceilinged room with walls reinforced by gray fiberglass. Immediately they were assailed by a unique mixture of smells—part decomposing wood, part sinigang—with a hint of gangrenous diabetic foot. Marjorie gawked at the variety of things on the floor—Coke bottles, huge plastic bags containing old receipts, old clothes, VHS tapes, cans, styrofoam from Wendy's all piled on top of each other, forming their very own Smoky Mountain.

"Dad's a collector, Marjorie," Mabel declared.

Marjorie laughed nervously, but she still managed to ask the questions that everyone had been asking all these years. Questions that were all fair, sensible, intelligent, and rational: Don't you have enough house personnel to take care of these things? Won't these catch fire? Won't these rodents cause disease? Why would he keep trash? Did you try to talk to him? Can't you throw these things out? Can't…

"Did you have any idea that he was this, umm, unique, when you were video messaging each other?" Smoketh asked Marjorie.

"Yes, ma'am."

The chandelier started to flicker. A tiny cockroach awkwardly flew and landed on the floor. Marjorie promptly ran after it, and after several attempts successfully stomped on it. She giggled at her own dexterity. From her vantage point Smoketh noticed how young Marjorie really looked, masked only by the pallor and emaciation from a lifetime of poverty, and probably a hint of latent tuberculosis.

"Then why did you still come here, Marjorie?" Mabel asked.

"Because I love him ma'am," she declared. "And I think… I think I can change him."

Mabel and Smoketh looked at each other, and, not too unkindly, burst out laughing.

Updates On Friendships And Miseries

MY CLAIRVOYANT FRIEND Namtab Pots announced that an asteroid will be hitting the earth in a few weeks. A quick Google search revealed that the information wasn't from his precognition, but from NASA. I opted not terrorize myself any further, so I avoided doing any research. I will just assume that one day, in the middle of flossing my teeth, a huge rock will crash through the roof and flatten me. Or worse, the rock will fall on me in the middle of getting extubated after surviving severe COVID pneumonia.

If I were to star in my own COVID tragedy movie, it would start on March 13, 2020. While going on rounds that morning I saw the usually perky Dr. Brittany May Santos frantically running along the hallways. She was wearing huge foggy goggles, a shower cap, and an N-95 mask. In the olden days a female doctor wearing N-95 would only make us conclude that she was pregnant. No formal pregnancy reveals were ever necessary in the hospital—that turquoise tight-fitting mask was the announcement, the pathognomonic sign, the trigger for juicy hospital rumors.

Brittany May accosted me and told me to go home.

"Go home!" she yelled. "Send your patients home! Go home now!"

"What's happening!" I asked with a shrill, trying to keep up with her italics and exclamation points. "I still have patients for chemotherapy today! Patient G is bleeding profusely, and I need to refer him to surgery!"

Brittany May insisted that I drop everything as soon as I can, and that I send dischargeable patients home. A sick-looking *balikbayan* from Italy has tested positive for the virus yesterday, she said. Before getting admitted she was spotted shivering and coughing and walking around the facility. She had lunch at the nearby mall. Once transferred to the ICU her lungs quickly started to fail and she eventually died, sending panic to everyone who had an encounter with her. That night Viber messages started going bonkers and caused everyone to freeze in fear. Doctors, some very close to us, died. Many of my cancer patients were crippled with anxiety and chose to postpone cancer treatment for as long as they could. After a few weeks of getting stuck in the bomb shelter, subsisting on ten-year old Spam and spicy tuna, we were able to slap some sense into ourselves. Our patients were asking if they could resume their treatments, so we started setting up our tele-consultation platforms.

One of my first patients online was Lola Murghana Palavi. She had undergone mastectomy a few weeks prior, and when I asked if the surgical site was healing properly, she immediately ripped off her shirt to show her scar and the remaining breast. She then went on to tell me about how she was able to clean the entire house and cook all sorts of fancy meals since the lockdown had started. She was also able to read a couple of books. And catch up on her crocheting. I reminded her that she could put her shirt back on.

I love my senior citizen patients. They always have great—albeit very long and intricate—stories to tell. They frequently laugh at my jokes, even the really off-color ones (they seem to prefer those). For them I am the most handsome doctor they've ever met, presbyopia and all. And in the pre-masking era, the best smelling, because no one but the really old grandmothers can get away with sniffing someone on the neck. One such patient, 75-year-old Mrs. Cokelya Mia, once told me that the radiation oncologist I had referred her to was very handsome. She must have thought that I found it offensive, so she quickly followed it up with a nervous, "I mean he's also handsome, like you, I mean, you're both handsome! Equally!" My secretary was also the prettiest woman she had ever seen. And all the chemo nurses, they were all gorgeous and dazzling. I would tell her, in return, that she always looked elegant and fresh. At some point, it became obvious that we were just bouncing flatteries off each other.

The most trying aspect of online consultation, of course, was the inability to do physical examination. We had to innovate, such as when I had to ask the patients to palpate their own necks and describe to me how the neck tumors felt. All of a sudden, I was a med school instructor teaching Physical Diagnostics on the first day of class–the forehead is "hard", the nose is "doughy". Certain instructions sounded terrible when taken out of context, such as "*Sige kapain mo. Sige pa! Matigas?*" or "Touch your right ball. Good. *Good.* Now shine a flashlight from under it." At some point I could only try to guess what was actually happening to the patient. I discovered that the "tele-" in teleconsultation actually refers to telepathy.

During the quiet moments of the lockdown, whenever I was not checking my temperature, inspecting my tonsils in the mirror, or revising my last will and testament, I would demand that my friends update me on their lives. If no one in the chat groups replied, I would say that I have a brand new chika as bait. My friend, pediatric pulmonologist Frichmond, informed us one morning that she was starting to go into labor. She was wheeled into the labor room with her face encased in a respirator mask, making her labor moans sound techno. While waiting for her third child to crawl out of her, she entertained herself by listening to a Zoom conference on pediatric asthma. Although these are trying times to bring a baby into the world, we decided to look at the silver lining: that Frichmond could just tell everyone that you are cordially not invited to the christening ceremonies, the first birthday, and all subsequent birthdays during the pandemic, saving her a lot of cash.

Meanwhile, at the Hall of The DSWD, Smoketh proudly declared that she had just cut her hair using the unicorn hair tie technique as instructed on Youtube. In the spirit of being the DSWD secretary, she asked us what first aid medications would be recommended for their new house help who was suffering from a burn injury on her chest. We tried, but nobody correctly guessed the cause of the burn injury: *nabanlian ng kumukulong bulalo*. We had so many questions, but this immediately called to mind an incident that happened years ago when we were still in residency training. Smoketh had accompanied Inay Leonora Corazon dela Riva, one of their senior kasambahay's, for a consult at the charity gastroenterology clinic. Inay Leonora Corazon had developed severe difficulty in swallowing, and they were afraid that a tumor could be blocking her esophagus. Upon endoscopy they discovered multiple santol seeds stuck in the sphincter leading into the stomach. In the monitor her esophagus looked like an excavation site blocked by multiple boulders after a trench collapse. Smoketh gasped audibly as she watched the gastroenterologist deftly harpoon each seed out of the stretched-out orifice. Apparently, swallowing whole santol seeds is more common than we think. It is a dangerous practice, as these seeds have a tendency to latch on to the lining of the gastrointestinal mucosa.

Somewhere in Antipolo, Helliza was gathering positive cosmic energy by taking a long break from social media. She became a much happier person as a result, not being exposed to the extreme politicization and competition of wit on Twitter. She is now catching up on Gossip Girl. Kathy, a dermatologist, has enrolled in an online business administration class based in Barcelona. She showed us a photo of her classmates, who all look like gorgeous telenovela actors. She plans to fly to Barcelona to attend the classes in person, as soon as travel restrictions are lifted. I suspect that she's planning to escape the Philippines. We all want to escape with her.

Dr. Abby Chan, a friend living in South Carolina, called me up one night to update me on the latest miseries in her life. I was sleepy, but she sounded very worried. Her husband, The Talented Mr. Len-

Len Chan, has been suffering from terrible nightmares the past few weeks. Abby thinks it's stress related. Len-Len is an intensive care specialist, and he has been getting very exhausted from all the critical COVID patients that he manages in the ICU. They live in an area where many people don't wear masks and choose not to get vaccinated in accordance with their inalienable rights. Their neighbors hold protest rallies outside municipal halls chanting, "We will not comply! We will not comply! We will not comply!"

I asked Abby to give me more details about the dreams, so we could interpret them together. Abby and I were psychology majors back in college, and we like to pretend that we still remember something from decades ago. The prominent imagery in Len-Len's recurrent nightmare is lava. A volcano explodes, there is wild egress of lava, and it disintegrates the neighboring communities. Earthquakes and natural calamities abound.

"Any Psych 101 student can tell you that it is a Freudian dream," I said with extreme condescension. "Lava. Hot, viscous liquid squirting all over. Get it, get it?"

"Hmmm."

"Come on."

"No, tell me."

"Your husband is aching to fuck, Abigail. The lava is cum. How the heck were you not able to figure it out? A volcano ruptures, boiling lava floods into the village, and seeps into the crevices. *Your* crevices!

The next time you throw his underwear in the washing machine try to check if…"

Abby told me to shut up, she got it. She was impressed. Her initial interpretation was that the lava represented respiratory secretions that were gushing and spraying all over, causing widespread COVID infections. Thanks to me, she realized she was wrong. She immediately whispered my insights to Len-Len, who was having ginseng chicken soup with their kids. Abby tried to explain in Filipino, so that the kids wouldn't get an unscheduled lecture on the psychic manifestations of unrealized fornication.

"*Ang panaginip mo daw ay sumisimbolo sa pagniniig,*" Abby whispered to Len-Len, who was off-camera. "And the lava is *ano… ano nga sa tagalog ang likido na lumalabas sa ari ng lalaki?*"

It took all my Catholic restraint not to press an imaginary game show buzzer and scream: "*Tamod! Tamod!!!*"

Hot Flash

"BAKIT ANG INET!" I yelled to Countess Anastacia Romanova, my clinic secretary. I wasn't being a jerk, but I had to scream across the room through two layers of face mask, an industrial-thick face shield, and an acrylic barrier. I had just finished doing chemo at the Cancer Center, and at 12 noon dashed under the sun to my private clinic located in another building. Five minutes in I felt like I was either going to turn blue from hypoxia, or burst into flames. Whoever implied that the summer heat would bake the virus dead must have meant that the heat would kill its hosts first.

"Sira ang aircon," The Countess harrumphed, as she furiously jotted on the patient logbook, furiously stapled papers, and furiously stamped documents with a rubber stamp. I had no doubt that she was busy, and the heat must also be turning her into a total loon, but I couldn't recall anything that required such desultory rubberstamping. But it made for a good visual on how busy she was.

"Kakaunti naman ang patients di ba? Di ba?" I asked.

"Nine," she said sternly, as she slammed the paper charts on my desk. Anxiety gripped my innards, sweat continued to pool in my pants, and my stomach started to growl as I stared at the thick sheaves of paper. I should have eaten more than an egg yolk for breakfast, I scolded myself.

After donning a fresh isolation gown the first patient came in: Mrs. Gerudias, 45 years old, diagnosed with breast cancer stage II. As I flipped through her lab results, I was hoping that she was negative for the breast cancer marker called "HER-2", as a positive result signals a more aggressive disease and requires more time for discussion. She was HER-2 positive. Explaining the schedules and the cost of the treatment, as well as the ways to finance it, took us an extra twenty minutes on our way to abject dehydration.

The fourth patient was Mrs. Munroe, 52 years old, also with breast cancer. She was accompanied by her kumare, Mrs. Gomez. My throat was starting to dry up, but I couldn't risk removing my mask to drink. I imagined COVID just floating in the air, waiting for me to make a mistake. Luckily, I was only wearing a t-shirt underneath the isolation gown, but it was starting to get soaked. This must be what hot flashes feel like, only this was continuous, and not just a flash. I never did figure out if it was hot flash or hot flush.

"*Ang hirap mag-menopause*," I quipped as I fanned my face with both hands. Nobody laughed or even courtesy-snickered.

I stayed silent for five more seconds. Maybe they would eventually laugh. Nothing.

Fine, I also want this to be over anyway, I thought, a bit hurt. They were also suffering and couldn't care less about any unnecessary attempts at levity. Fine.

I started to palpitate, maybe from an impending heat stroke, maybe hunger. I hoped the patients wouldn't ask too many questions just for this day, until we get this ancient air conditioner fixed. Or until we pull the damn thing out and throw it in the fire. This was very reminiscent of that one intense summer day during our internal medicine residency, when the air conditioner in our call room suddenly conked out and led to everyone in the batch to start whining. For one whole day we would moan, complain, and bitch at each other. Finally my batchmate Ruter snapped. He took off his shirt, unscrewed the useless aircon, and threw the damn thing out of the room by himself. Magically, he also made a brand new aircon appear. We, the whiners, were exhilarated.

After almost half an hour of consult, Mrs. Munroe said that she was satisfied with my detailed explanation on the ins and outs of chemotherapy. She seemed intent on starting her treatment in two days. She was about to leave, when her *kumare*, Mrs. Gomez, suddenly remembered something. She brought out a pile of printed materials and asked:

"*Pero may nabasa ako sa internet, mas lalong umiiksi ang buhay, dahil ang chemotherapy ay pumapatay ng bad cells and good cells.* Can you clarify if… what if, supposing…."

I had three options: A) Be all condescending, lose my temper, blame the heat, get video-recorded, and be *cancelledt* forever. B) Pretend to pass out in pure dehydration or C) Compartmentalize, summon patience and other virtues, be a total Mother Theresa.

I didn't get a chance to choose.

"*Itatanong na lang namin yan during chemo, lalabas na kami, ang init!*" Mrs. Munroe said, as she pulled her kumare out of the clinic.

Thank you, Mrs. Munroe!

Collapse

THE PAPER STRAW IN MY ICED COFFEE started to collapse. I had left this cup on the counter of numerous nurse stations, brought it inside patients' rooms, and lugged it around from one hospital wing to another. After the fifth patient, coffee started to crawl up the straw, turning it into mush. Metal or bamboo straws were not an option. I tried using these eco-friendly weapons when they were all the rage years ago, and at one point I almost impaled my hard palate with stainless steel while sipping and driving on a dirt road.

I had resolved to always finish my coffee before going on hospital rounds, trying to convince myself that for thirty minutes cancer can wait. The cancer would still be there, whether I go on rounds at 8 or 8:30. But it was a particularly busy day, made more difficult by the necessary logistical maze of COVID-prevention protocols. Realizing the sort of antibiotic-resistant bugs that might already be swimming in my watered-down coffee I threw it in the trash along with the macerated straw. Taking your drink around the hospital was a disgusting practice anyway. By now I should be used to the idea that when I slap an N-95 mask on, the next time I would be removing it is when I drive home.

I went through the text messages that I received that morning. Patient Ethan, a 22-year-old former soccer player, said that the low back pain that had been lingering for weeks had suddenly disappeared. "Like a miracle," he gushed. For weeks we'd been communicating virtually for pain management. It was the height of the COVID surge, and he couldn't compete with the lines of patients snaking outside the ER. Lung cancer, which had spread to his liver, had also munched on his vertebrae, threatening a debilitating complication called spinal cord compression. I had been e-mailing him prescriptions for steroids, morphine, fentanyl, and all sorts of things to help with the pain while waiting for a more definitive treatment, but his pain scale went down to at best a 4/10. When the logistics finally allowed for him to undergo radiation therapy, he contracted mild COVID. This caused a two-week delay before he could undergo treatment that on all accounts should be considered an emergency. The news that his low back pain had suddenly disappeared filled me with joy, for one second.

"Can you still move your legs?" I asked.

He couldn't, not even side to side. He had lost all sensation, including bladder and bowel control. He was paralyzed. The spinal cord compression was complete.

This was my fourth case of spinal cord compression during the pandemic. It was the worst time to get afflicted with this oncologic emergency, or any medical emergency for that matter. It was difficult to admit patients for something as simple as intravenous steroid administration or pain management. Rehabilitation referral, brace fitting, orthopedic evaluation, physical therapy–all of these were forced to take a back seat. The mandatory COVID testing further delayed things. After that one case of spinal cord compression back in residency that got us audited for not moving fast enough, I'd always tried to be hyper-vigilant with these cases. This time, hyper-vigilance got me nowhere.

We successfully secured a hospital room for Ethan when his COVID cleared, and he was finally able to start treatment. I told him, with much apprehension, that it might be too late to regain the use of his legs, but we could still hope. With the forced precocity of someone about to die, or maybe because he really just had a better outlook in life, Ethan told me not to be too sad about it. That it's ok. It kills me whenever this strange role reversal happens.

A few weeks later, when the surge died down, teenagers started crawling back to the malls, doing the things they always loved to do. Standing on a chair to get a better photo of a bowl of ramen. Snapping a group-fie with the centerpiece installation of the mall, tongues sticking to the side, finger hearts all over. Vlogging about an elaborate, colorful dessert that probably tasted like crap. I used to get irritated at these kids, secretly judging how shallow they were, sneering at all their efforts for social media content. They must be vapid and stupid. But taking care of young patients like Ethan, who had suffered so much in their short lives, forced me to reevaluate this arrogance. Ethan should be doing a selfie with a frappucino, not wasting away in the wards, waiting if a pulmonary embolism or aspiration pneumonia will kill him first.

I always tried to avoid getting too introspective when my patients die, but news that Ethan had died after coughing out buckets of blood reinforced my fear of what we'd always known: that we have such a limited time on this planet. Makes you want to call up your friends to say: go and take all the mall selfies that you want. Be ridiculous and corny and unapologetic. Ignore the haughty, condescending spectators. Live.

Moments

AT AROUND 9 AM my friend, Dr. Love, picked me up from the Cancer Care Center, and we ran to the Manila Med penthouse for our second dose of the COVID vaccine. It took us some time—very few people were allowed to use the elevator together, causing long lines along the hospital corridors. The quarantine restrictions borne out of the March 2021 surge were slowly getting lifted, and people were already coming to the hospital in droves. By the time we reached the penthouse a crowd, composed of healthcare workers and non-medical staff, had already formed in the lobby. Seeing many familiar faces after a year of limited interactions had transformed us into temporary extroverts, but we had to restrain ourselves from making too much *chika*. Laughing and braying were still considered weapons of mass destruction.

I reported to the screener that after the first dose my right arm had turned all red and firm for a few days. It was so red that I had to call up Dr. Rose Zamora, an infectious disease expert, to ask if I needed strong antibiotics for a possible gas gangrene. The inflammation subsided on its own after ten days. After that first dose I also became very hungry, eating everything on sight. Asking around, I found out that only one other person had experienced the same "side effect", so most probably it was something that we just made up.

While lining up, Love and I gossiped about some of our med school batchmates. We tried. We realized that we were of that age when the usual gossip fodder of who was pregnant, or who had broken-up were no longer thrilling, so we settled for some very light news.

One of our classmates, Calypso Jean Villacorta, recently called me to ask for an opinion about a malignancy. She sounded quite strange on the phone. Her words were very deliberate and apologetic, as if she wanted to make sure that she did not, in any way, sound offensive, or that she wasn't taking up too much of my time. She sounded, in fact, like a junior trainee endorsing a case to a terror consultant. She even texted beforehand: "Doc, is it okay to call *po*?"

"Why did she sound like that?" I asked Love. "It makes me so sad! Weren't we, like... friends?" Truly, there was no shortage of opportunities to be dramatic and shine the spotlight yet again on little, old me.

Come to think of it, I couldn't recall a particular moment when I had a substantial interaction with Calypso Jean. According to a wise friend, JP Bowzung, one can categorize a person as a "friend" when you have experienced a "moment" together. Maybe you happened to catch each other buying pornographic DVD along Pedro Gil, or you caught each other smoking in the ambulance parking lot when you should be manning the ICU. Or you discovered that you both hated the same person, because nothing brings doctors closer together than shared enmity towards a horrible senior. No matter how seemingly insignificant or embarrassing, if you both feel that there is a connection, then that singular moment instantly catapults you into some level of friendship.

I never had that with Calypso Jean. Still, my default mode whenever I interact with a batchmate in a working environment is one of instant overfamiliarity, aka "feeling close". Like it's the safer stance that I can just downgrade if unreciprocated. Others don't operate that way. When I was a senior fellow, I gave a CT scan request to a patient, with my name and signature on it. The exasperated patient handed the rejected request back to me after she had walked all the way from radiology. She pointed to an underlined note from the radiology resident, a batchmate in med school: To the fellow, please fill-up the history and physical examination portions of the request form completely.

Well!

"Even in the operating room, I always find it easier to work with those from our class, even if we weren't particularly close," Love said. As a plastic surgeon, Love had to work with a team of other surgeons and anesthesiologists, some of whom were our med school friends.

Love and I had been friends since med school, but recently we had what might be considered a supplementary moment, ensuring that in a few years I won't feel too embarrassed asking her for a face lift, a tummy tuck, cheek implants, a butt lift, and so on. This moment happened back in 2019, when I felt like things were starting to go well for me. I was happy with my work schedule, and the patient load was just right. I was able to read a lot of books, and months had passed without me obsessing that I could be harboring an occult tumor. But of course, as soon as the idea that things were great had even crossed my mind, something horrific was bound to ruin it.

One night, while removing my unusually tight pants by lazily pushing them down with my feet, I lost my balance and hit my left eye on the metal edge of a chair. Obviously, nothing major, I thought, as I struggled to stand up. I was in my own room where it was safe, after all. And then I saw bright, red blood dripping on the floor, slowly at first, followed by an extravagant gush. I immediately ran to the mirror and saw a 3-inch gaping wound with jagged edges, traversing my left eyebrow. In a matter of seconds, it started acting up like a ripped placenta, spurting blood on the mirror, on the sink, on my clothes, all over.

"Love, can I call you," I messaged Love. She immediately called me and inquired, in a soft, calm voice, "What happened? Are you alone? Are you drunk? Are you in an abandoned corner lot in Malate?" I insisted that I wouldn't let anybody but her do surgery on my face, and that I would wait until sunrise when the clinic opens.

"You have to save my looks. They're all I have," I whimpered, in pure drama. I slept with a humongous block of ice resting on my face.

The next morning, on Valentine's Day, Love sewed me up. It was a very deep cut. As she was suturing the muscles underneath the skin, I narrated once more the idiotic story of how I got the injury.

"OK. But what really happened?" she asked.

For about a month I conducted lectures, made rounds, did chemo, and attended conferences wearing a gigantic pair of sunglasses to cover up my raccoon eyes. I was frequently asked "what happened", and with each re-telling the story had evolved into something grander.

"So, I was taking off my pants," I started telling Dr. Deo, who was writing on a patient's chart in the nurses' station. He interrupted me and decided to continue the story himself. "So you were in a motel, you were too excited to have sex, you hurriedly took off your pants, and fell on the floor!"

The only proper reply, in front of all the nurses, was, "Yes, Deo. Yes, that's exactly what happened."

After the video orientation on the benefits of vaccination, we finally received our injections. I imagined antibodies swiftly getting recruited, swirling around in my system, rehearsing what they would do if COVID managed to sneak in. The rehearsal would take about two weeks. All I had to do was survive the other threats to my life, like an entire building crashing down on me in an earthquake, or contracting Creutzfeldt-Jakob Disease. After the vaccination I immediately told my friends Ruth Marks, Jason, and Rex that I had already received my second dose. Maybe they would be happy for me, now that I can safely go about with my responsibilities as a healthcare worker. Or maybe they would be secretly envious. Maybe they would congratulate me, or ask about the immediate side effects, which would be an opportunity for me to turn it into a teachable moment. Maybe...

"*Pwede ka nang makipag-duraan,*" Jason said.

Adulthood, Datehood,
Fertilehood, Ghosthood

RIGHT BEFORE THE PANDEMIC STRUCK, my good friend Claudette
F. was introduced to Paulo T. through a common friend. Claudette
had just broken up with her boyfriend of six months, and she needed
someone "to cleanse her palate". Not the noblest romantic intention, she
admitted, and it was like courting bad karma. But she had just bought
a black midriff blouse and she was ready to open her heart once again.
Claudette and Paulo started spending a lot of time online.

Initially Paulo did not really make much of an impact, but he
was so into her and that was all Claudette ever really needed. She
insisted to her friends that she was obsessed with his sexy, moustached
daddy look. Nobody really asked, but she went on with the thesis
statement that if you look at the different parts of his body, none of
those parts may immediately pop out as conventionally delectable. But
that if you go beyond the perversion of objectifying body parts, and
look at the whole picture instead, like an Austrian gestalt psychologist,
then you will realize how beautiful he really is. Absolutely nobody
agreed, and we assured her that none of us were objectifying him. We
started to wonder why she was getting preemptively defensive.

Claudette had one bad thing to say about Paulo. She disclosed
that he has never watched a single episode of her favorite sitcom,
The Office, but that he possesses an extensive knowledge of the
filmography of one buxom Sandra Keisha Kay, a Persian-American

porn star. I started to argue that being a porn connoisseur is in no way inferior to someone who binges on well-written sitcoms, if they are at all even remotely comparable. Clearly, I was just trying to be a good friend by being patronizing.

Every time Claudette goes out with someone new, we start to worry. She doesn't have the most impressive dating record, so one can argue that she might be the one at fault for all her romantic failures. That she is too picky, or that her friends are too critical, as if we are raving beauties ourselves. Once, at the height of loneliness, Claudette announced that she had sufficiently lowered her dating standard to "*basta humihinga*". Not to be outdone, Jean, another friend with a horrendous dating history, revealed her much lower standard: "*kahit naka-mechanical ventilator*". We gave Claudette our unsolicited blessing to go out on a date with this Paulo for yet another "learning experience".

Claudette and Paulo met in person for the first time around Valentines. Claudette was relieved to learn that Paulo has depth. He writes poetry. He can make latté art. He was the president of a student organization back in college. Throughout the dinner Claudette found herself falling more and more in love with him, and when Paulo said that he can actually do parkour, her once dormant oocytes started wriggling and popping into accelerated fertilehood. She gloated and started imagining how embarrassed her shallow friends would be when she tells us how we had terribly misjudged him.

After gorging on paella Claudette and Paulo walked around the Malate area. They had a couple of drinks, ate each other's faces, and had heavy petting in the parking lot of Robinson's. Just as Paulo's hand was crawling up Claudette's thigh, Claudette whispered that she couldn't have sex just yet, that night being their first date. And most definitely not inside a car! So they scheduled a second date. In her head: "As an independent, responsible adult capable of sound decision-making and restraint, I am going to have sex on the second date".

And then the pandemic happened.

So, there was no second date, everyone was locked inside their houses, and there was that hanging prospect of sexual intercourse that should have happened but didn't. She told herself that of course we would still talk online and such. But through the course of the hard lockdown Claudette started sensing that something was amiss. Something had suddenly changed. Paulo was no longer messaging her as much as he used to, and he was not liking her posts anymore. She would ask for his pre-sleeping selfie but he wouldn't ask for hers. His replies went from "okay" to "ok" to "k". Claudette started rummaging online for the latest recommendation on the conduct of sexual intercourse in the middle of a pandemic, just in case Paulo springs a surprise booty call. She found an article, complete with an infographic attachment, demonstrating that lovers can still have sex as long as they wear surgical masks. I told her that what she had read might actually be fringe porn.

"Maybe he's busy, but I'm sure he still thinks about you," I assured her, followed by other platitudes and beautiful, blatant lies. But Claudette wasn't a fool, and she had already gone through the whole laborious process of investigating and over-interpreting every little aspect of Paulo's online behavior. She was inconsolable for days.

Claudette has given me the permission to share this cautionary tale, as long as I change enough details without altering the spirit of the jilting and ghosting process. In faux-therapist mode I asked her if she can pinpoint the specific cause of distress in this whole ugly experience with Paulo. I gave her 3 choices:

A) She is distressed because Paulo is really the one. Just because he doesn't fit the mold of what she–or anyone in the universe for that matter–likes, doesn't mean that he can't be a fantastic husband and father to their children.

B) She is distressed because for all his addiction to porn he is actually the perfect guinea pig on which she can test her ability to transform people and improve mankind. PS: Nobody really believed that he could create latté art or do parkour.

C) She is distressed because they almost had sex, and she wanted to have sex with him that night, but pretended that she didn't want to.

Obviously I only suggested this option as a mean joke, knowing full-well Claudette's stand on issues, *womynhood*, independence, femininity...

"C! C of course! C C C!!!" Claudette said. "C!"

Get Out

I WAS HOLDING A TRAY full of reconstituted chemo meds, and I realized that if I so much as sneeze and drop everything on the floor, and the bottles break, or remain intact and roll to the other end of the room, only to be run over by a speeding wheelchair while everyone in the chemo unit gasps in terror—if all those things that could only be expressed in a run-on sentence happened—then I would need to sell a property (like my house) to replace everything. On today's menu: pembrolizumab for melanoma, pertuzumab and trastuzumab for breast cancer, bevacizumab for colon cancer, and brentuximab vedotin for Hodgkin lymphoma. Also on the tray–the now relatively cheap docetaxel, which, around ten years ago, was one of the most expensive chemotherapy drugs available. It is still pretty costly at around P15,000 a pop, but it's peanuts compared to the deluxe monoclonal antibodies and the ultra-deluxe immunotherapy. More new drugs, more options, more dilemma. In extreme hypochondriation I started hoarding insurance policies like crazy, just in case I would need to use these meds for myself in the future. Selling my action figures is not an option. There are vultures already circling the sky for my rare 2007 DC Direct Wonder Woman action figure based on the art of Terry Dodson, as well as my magnificent Silver Age Legion of Superheroes action figure set. They come to the grave with me!

I once attended a convention in Madrid where a pharmaceutical company formally unveiled the final data for a new lung cancer molecule after years of rigorous clinical trials. The data was so impressive it got a standing ovation—the last time I saw such an overwhelming upswell of emotion was when The Undertaker defeated Yokozuna in a casket match in Survivor Series 1994. In actual practice this new drug is indeed magnificent, amazing, fantastic, and astonishing, and all my patients using it have so far exhibited good disease control. If only more people can afford it without having to go bankrupt, a key event that eventually leads to nasty disputes among family members.

One of my least favorite scenarios in the clinic is when children start fighting over the medical care of an elderly parent. There are two extreme scenarios: the parent has no money and nobody wants to take care of her, or the parent is too wealthy and the kids are prematurely quarrelling over who gets the floundering resort and the diamond earrings. Whenever this drama unfolds inside the clinic I cringe and pretend to look at the ceiling, or make like I'm gathering gems from my online village games. After a few minutes, I force a smile, which comes out as a wince.

At least for weeping patients I can offer tissue paper as a gesture, but for bickering adults I can't think of anything I can give that will signify: Take your issues outside! Or if I'm in a zen mood: Take a deep breath and listen to your breath, doesn't it totally sound like the ocean?

One such patient with bickering family members was 65-year-old Mrs. Minerva Faye Drosophilla. During the initial consult her two kids dredged up personal issues that covered decades of resentment, and eventually they stopped coming with her in any of her follow-up consults. She had very little savings of her own, so imagine my relief when it turned out that she still had an existing citizenship in Denmark. It was my cue to tell Mrs. Minerva Faye Drosophilla: get out!

After six months of chemotherapy under my care, I was able to convince her to continue her treatment in Denmark. She had been working as a chef in a posh hotel in Copenhagen for over 20 years, and she only came back to the Philippines for a vacation. It was during this vacation that she had noted a lump on her breast, and work-up revealed that it was a malignant tumor that had already spread to her lungs and bones. I told her that she must leave as soon as she was strong enough and all her documents were in place. In Denmark she could receive all the ideal medications under her comprehensive medical insurance. The regretful thing is that all those drugs are available here in the Philippines and there is no shortage of expertise, but everything should be paid out-of-pocket. So far, government insurance coverage for chemotherapy has been extremely limited.

Mrs. Minerva and I would occasionally communicate in Facebook, and on the rare occasion that I would post something about myself she would like, comment, and share it using her two Facebook accounts. Except when my post was about action figures, she didn't care much for those.

I recently posted a photo of myself posing in front of our brand-new Mary Mediatrix Cancer Institute, and immediately I saw that there was "1 Share". I clicked on it and saw that it was a token share by my sister. Mrs. Minerva should have shared this twice by now, I told myself, so I went to her page, a bit concerned. And true enough, on her profile page were messages of condolences, reminiscences about her life, photos of how she looked when she was healthy, photos of the gourmet cuisine she had cooked. She had died in Copenhagen only two weeks ago.

Recently more and more patients have been using social media as their preferred mode of communication (a patient once complained of severe abdominal pains via my Instagram account, which has nothing but photos of action figures). I sometimes click on their profile to see what they are like outside the clinic, and for sure they also check mine. Some patients post fund-raising efforts. Some work in Krusty Krab. Some are big fans of nasty revisionist history videos. Regardless of the kind of life they lead, it is refreshing to see that they have an identity apart from being a cancer patient.

I once had a social media savvy patient, Lilibeth Hyacinth, who was terminally ill from an aggressive form of lymphoma. She had been in the hospital for over a month, and the expenses were piling up. A day before she died, she posted on Facebook a photo of the food her mom had bought from the sidewalk vendors along Faura:

a tiny piece of fried fish and rice wrapped in plastic. It would be her last meal. Her caption was: *Wala na talaga kaming pera*. Going through her photo albums I saw that she used to join barangay beauty contests. She also liked sewing clothes with her mother. She loved the sea.

Being friends with patients on social media adds an extra degree of heartbreak when they die. You are able to see how they were in their youth, back when they were full of life, and when they had no idea that a random mutation would alter the course of their lives beyond their control. You can also see that there were people who loved them dearly, people who are now in pain.

The New Preamble

SMOKETH HAS FINALLY FINISHED her Master's thesis. So, on top of being a nephrologist, an antique curator, and a former model, she is now a faculty member of the Department of Physiology. When we were in first year med school, we were all terrified of the nephrology physiology module, finding all those transporters and tubules too confusing. And of course, sodium. I never understood sodium. I have long given up on the intricacies of sodium and just assume that it has a mind of its own, going wherever it wants to go: in, out, with water, without water.

The results of our first-year med kidney physiology examination were released on a hot and humid February 28 in BSLR East. I remember, because there were two of us in class celebrating our invisible leap year birthdays that day, me and Mildred. After the class had languidly sung a tokenistic Happy Birthday (they just wanted to get to the exam results, dang it), Dr. Cordelia, the nephrology consultant, went in front and said, "I'm so sorry that the exam was so difficult. But it's not my fault, *ha*, it was Dr. Manuelita's!" Dr. Manuelita was the other nephrologist in charge of the exam.

"But even though the exam was difficult, someone got 98%!" Dr. Cordelia said. "Congratulations are in order for the topnotcher, the birthday girl herself, Mildred!"

The room exploded in cheers and gasps of disbelief. Mildred looked quite calm during the exam, but she didn't look too confident. In fact, we were expecting that Krueger de Mesa would top it, after all the spectacle he had created. During the exam he kept on mumbling "Yes! Yes!" while pumping his fists, unmindful that we were shooting him annoyed stares. Finally, Irene could no longer take it and screamed, "*Pwede ba!*" That shut him up. Years later, when we were much mature, my friend Ditz and I would pump our fists and scream a guttural "Yes! Yes! Yes! Woooh!" during difficult exams just to infuriate everyone.

"Congratulations, birthday girl!" Dr. Cordelia repeated. I expected my classmates to look and sneer at the visibly dejected Krueger, who was pretending to be busy with his fingernails. But instead they all looked at me, assuming that *I* should be feeling pressured. Why, because we shared the same birthday?

"*Matatalino daw talaga pag leap year! Ahahaha!*" Dr. Cordelia laughed, deliberately making more *gatong*.

Well, you know what Dr. Cordelia and the entire class, I wasn't feeling pressured at all! Because I knew deep in my heart of hearts that I had totally fucked that exam!

After the top five were announced Dr. Cordelia displayed the complete list of results on the bulletin board. I got a failing grade of 55%, which meant that I had to take the finals at the end of the semester. I also failed one exam each in all the other subjects, so I had to take all the final exams. They called such unfortunate lot the grand finalists.

To celebrate her liberation from thesis data collection and statistical analysis, Smoketh and I decided to buy a keyboard for her tablet. Smoketh abhors shopping, and she needs a constant enabler who will stop her from talking herself out of a purchase. While waiting for her in Coffee Bean in UP Town Center I decided to go back to a manuscript I was writing. A college guy, Benito, was also typing furiously on his Mac at the next table. His date, Wesley, then arrived. Wesley was extremely apologetic for being late, and from the way they were talking, their very polite and conscious usage of words, the courtesy laughter at each other's jokes, I concluded that it was the first time that they were meeting in person. This meant that I could no longer go on writing, because I had to concentrate on this nefarious habit of eavesdropping.

But was it really eavesdropping, pray tell, if our tables were so close to each other, that their laughter could dangerously shower SARS COV 2-laced spittle on my non-fat latte with two sachets of Stevia? Was it really eavesdropping, if they were talking so loudly, as if in a one-act play that deserved a standing O? The answer, of course, is yes. It's a bad habit. I should be using my earphones more often. More focus, less snooping, greater productivity. But their lives are so exciting *kase*!

Wesley excused himself to talk to someone on the phone. When he got off the call, he told Benito that it was the laboratory where he had his COVID swab test done yesterday.

"They just called to tell me I'm negative," Wesley beamed. "So have you had your vaccine *na*?"

So, I guess vaccination status now becomes part of the new preamble on post-apocalyptic/still-apocalyptic dating. On top of "I have a job", "I'm against red-tagging and extra-judicial killings", and "I don't have an STD".

Summer Thirst

I ONCE TOLD MY FRIEND Dr. Benny dela Costa of that horrific summer of my youth, when I was forced to bear false witness and pretend that I was possessed by the spirit of Tessie. It was a story I loved telling friends who could endure long, self-indulgent soliloquies, and with each retelling I felt guiltier and guiltier. Benny, however, was not impressed, and responded by telling me about the most miserable, hormone-ravaged summer of his youth. Competitiveness in misery: the hallmark of being a total drama queen.

His story, of course, also started in the summer of '92, when he had just completed fifth grade from The Temple of the Holy Spirit. He prefaced his tale with a list of the awards he had received: an honorable mention, Second Best in English, and most deliciously, Best in Religion. These prestigious accolades made him feel like he was entitled to demand for the best summer ever. A year earlier he had already finished the ritual of circumcision, and his grown-up penis was raring to experience its first summer. He was looking forward to going on camping trips and smoking his first cigarette, but most of all, he was excited to strip down naked and run to the beach with Leslie, the girl of his dreams. The *satanista* craze that had caused collective dread among the student body was already cooling down. They all realized that the nuns, of all people, had concocted this fantastic tale of cultish *satanistas* who would grab the students' eyeballs as they ate *isaw* on the pavement. The real scions of Satan, they would later realize, were just waiting in the wings, because in a few days the election campaign period of 1992 would start, heralded by a symphony of very corny jingles.

"This is a worst summer ever," his brother, college student Michael, whimpered, as he fanned himself with an old newspaper. He always carried that particular copy with him. They would later find out that it contains the "sex-ploits" of the everyday man as narrated by the trailblazing Xerex Xaviera. The national brown outs had already extended to almost twelve punishing hours a day, and Benny had absolutely nothing to do other than complain, play jackstones with his younger sister Marissa, and pore through allergic rhinitis-inducing copies of Readers' Digests. Most of the time they would just make a vigil beside the dead television, ready to take command of it as soon as the electricity comes back on. In other words, time better spent praying the rosary, the nuns would say.

"We have absolutely no money for any excursion this summer," Benny's mother, Mrs. Minerva said. She then went into a litany of all the things they needed in the house, all the tuition fees for the upcoming schoolyear, the food all five kids had to stuff in their needy faces just to stay alive, and how dare they even suggest that they eat in a restaurant, nobody's setting foot in any restaurant unless they are planning to wait tables! They did not have a term yet to adequately capture the stone-cold, sneering expression that accompanied such grand pronouncements. It would take decades for someone to accurately describe it, and truly it was the prototype for what would later be known as the Resting Cunt Face. Said resting cunt face would never budge, and Benny knew that if he was going to enjoy that damn summer—long brown outs and all—he would have to take charge.

Benny was able to sneak out that night to run to the town *perya*. For years he had been nurturing a crush on his classmate, Leslie, and he knew she would be in the *perya*. Her parents owned one of the rides, the Caterpillar, and when the schoolyear ended, she was tasked to man the ticket booth.

Benny waved at her from behind the trees. Even as she was slowly running towards him, with the widest smile, plump breasts bouncing wildly, he was already getting a half-erection. He handed her a pink cotton candy, most of which he had already eaten on his way to meet her. He had been desperately in love with her since they were in grade 3, the sort of painful love that he had to endure daily. In his head he was a long-suffering adult with a full-on, bushy beard signifying his world-weariness. He had so much love, so much libido, crammed into a pubertal mass of broiling hormones.

Leslie De Villa was not only incredibly pretty. She was also very smart, very ahead of her time. She claimed to have read the very sophisticated literature of Sidney Sheldon and Judith McNaught, while her contemporaries were stuck reading Nancy Drew reprints. While growth spurt was unkind to most of the girls who had turned bow-legged and incredibly pimply, Leslie De Villa's breasts had filled up to such enormous proportions that for months they were all Benny could think about.

"Thanks for the cotton candy, Benny, but what are you doing here?" she asked.

"To see you, Leslie. I've sneaked out and used up most of my summer allowance to buy that cotton candy, so I can spend some time with you."

"As I've told you, Benny, I can't go out with you."

"Why? It's the summer! Let's go to the beach!"

"I can't go out with you, Benny, because you're poor."

"What are you talking about... we're eleven! I just want to watch a movie or swim, we're not going to elope!"

Leslie muttered some platitudes, something meant to be a consolation prize. But Benny didn't care for those vacuous words. Or maybe he was just getting dizzy from being rejected outright—he had walked through the bush straight into the smooth swing of her sword that sliced cleanly through his neck. His eyes blurred, his ears rang, the children's laughter swirling with the megaphoned invitations to play balloon darts, watch the mutant mermaid from Sorsogon, or feed the paralytic cannibal some live chickens. Benny noticed that Leslie's face was getting redder, so he walked out on her, cock-blocked, completely frustrated. Leslie always had that cute mestiza flush the adults were so fond of. Benny would learn later on that it was a sign of lupus, and in ten years or so she would die from its complications.

The next day Benny's parents visited a relative to ask for a loan for the coming schoolyear's tuition fees. Michael supposedly went to a resort in Pansol with his best friend Albert. Benny was alone, completely dejected, drenched in sweat because of the scheduled power failure once again. He was replaying in his head how that encounter with Leslie couldn't have possibly gone any worse. Maybe he should have been more subtle. He started to write a profound love poem in an attempt to purge himself of his desires: Oh, Leslie/dear Leslie/your vagina…

Luckily the lights came back on. In his melancholy he knew there was only one thing left to do. He rushed to his father's cabinet where he kept his comprehensive collection of Guinness Book of World Records, and carefully removed them. There he found the goldmine: a Betamax copy of Interracial Sluts Part 4. He never watched porn before, but as his classmate Rodrigo had told him, it would change the way you look at things forever.

Benny plugged the Betamax and pushed the cassette in, his heart racing so fast, his tummy getting all sorts of cramps, sweat forming continents on his shirt. He could barely see any image at first, then some blue green filter flickered on the screen for about a minute or so. And then it started. Two buxom women in matching bikinis, a Caucasian and a Japanese, were walking in the forest, laughing their hearts out. They sat on the muddy field and drenched themselves in mud, still laughing. Caucasian woman screamed "wooh!" as she stripped away her bikini top and smeared mud on her bare boobs.

More giggling. Japanese woman screamed "wooh!", and so on. Benny actually found all the mud bathing kind of gross. And who should walk in in the middle of their *hilarious* conversation, but a nude African-American guy with the girthiest tree trunk for a penis. And that was the universe's cue to punish him for his obscene appetites, by turning off the power once again. Yes, the blackout had resumed.

Don't panic, Benny told himself, even as his left eyelid started to twitch. Surely there were smart ways to deal with the situation. Calm ways, systematic ways. But instead of doing any of those, he ran to the toolbox, took out a screwdriver, and unscrewed the top casing of the Betamax. What confronted him was a highly organized tray of nuts, bolts, and metal rods creating an impenetrable fortress to protect Interracial Sluts Part 4. Benny stabbed the cassette with the screwdriver, fished out a portion of the tape, and tried pulling the spool of tape out. Before long he had vivisected the entire damn machine, the carcass spread out on the floor. In a few minutes his parents and his siblings would come back and discover that their honorable mention son, who was the 1992 Best in Religion, was jacking off to a porno.

"In the first place, you should never have kept a bold film in this house. You're disgusting, Bernard!" Mrs. Minerva scolded his father. They hadn't confronted Benny yet. They were holding a top-secret family conference, aka motherly monologue, with Benny's filthy proclivities as the sole agenda. Benny pressed his ear firmly on the door and heard the phrases "temple of the holy spirit", "boyhood phase", and his favorite, "drug addiction".

"We must keep this among ourselves and not embarrass him any further," his father said with suspicious equanimity that could only be interpreted as an attempt at self-preservation. "I'm sure he learned his lesson, that you don't need pornography to get off!"

"Jesus Christ!" Mrs. Minerva screamed.

"It's just a little dirty movie, mom," Benny's older brother Michael said, "I have seen a couple of dirty movies and I turned out okay. The only difference is whenever I watch it I sorta, kinda focus my attention on the hot muscular guy. I guess what I'm trying to say, mom, dad, is that…"

Mrs. Minerva almost burst an aneurysm.

Benny rushed back to his room, consumed with anguish. He jumped to his bed and felt the very warm, damp bedsheet. The room, in the middle of the brownout, felt like cheap sauna, but he just lay on the bed and gazed at the luminous stick-on stars that peppered the ceiling. How would Leslie react at this exposed perversion? How thickly would his mother lay the guilt and for how long would she weaponize it? All of a sudden Benny felt tears streaming down the corners of his eyes, as he murmured, "fuck this summer".

ACKNOWLEDGEMENTS

Many of the stories in this collection are about my friends, and I will forever be thankful to them for allowing me the pleasure of turning them into caricatures without threats of violent retaliation. Smoketh, Mrs. T, Alanis Cornucopia, No To Thero Thomments, The Double-Headed D's, and my batchmates in med school, residency, and fellowship have led such interesting lives, I feel like I am being outshined in my own book.

I wish to thank the Bienvenido N. Santos Creative Writing Center for allowing me to participate in its 1st Creative Nonfiction Writing Workshop on Pathography: Writing the Pandemic, and personally to Professor Marjorie Evasco for her kindness and generosity. Thank you to the panelists, Lance Catedral and Joti Tabula, and to the writing fellows, for such an engaging and awe-inspiring workshop in the middle of a health crisis. Big thanks to Dr. Alice Sun-Cua, Elvie Razon-Gonzalez, Catherine Torres, Ging Zamora, Marissa Lim, Cel Aquino-Felipe, Pamela Patdu, Ardee Lugo, Kristine Tumabiene, Therese Lladoc-Natividad, Salie Barnuevo, Rex Monteverde, Eliza Dejoras, Kathy Reyes, Angeli Espiritu, Agnes Cariaga, Rosalina de los Reyes, Eduardo Liangco, and Abe Navarro-Lim for enduring the early, clunky versions of the manuscript. To Jessica Zafra, thank you for encouraging me to write about being a physician. I hadn't written anything new in a long time, but ever since I joined the writing bootcamp years ago I couldn't get myself to shut up. Thank you, Atty. Andrea Pasion-Flores and everyone at Milflores Publishing, for giving me the opportunity to share these stories.

To the *Philippine Star*, where the story "Secret Origins" first appeared, my sincerest gratitude.

And to our beloved mentors and patients at the UP College of Medicine, PGH Department of Internal Medicine, and PGH Division of Medical Oncology, I will forever be indebted for the inspiration, the life lessons, the sorrows, and the joys.

WILFREDO LIANGCO

is a medical oncologist who obtained his medical degree at the UP College of Medicine and trained in internal medicine and medical oncology at the Philippine General Hospital. When he is not holding clinics or taking photos of his action figures, he writes about his friends who (mostly) consent to the caricaturization of their lives. He likes reading fiction and comic books, distressing over non-issues, hypochondriating, and remembering things that don't matter. His essays and short stories have appeared in *The Philippine Star*, *The Philippines Free Press*, *Health and Lifestyle Magazine*, and *The Philippines Graphic*. He writes at www.wilfredoliangco.com. Follow him on Instagram at @willliangco.

This book's typeface is set using Minion Pro and Gotham. Minion Pro is designed by Robert Slimbach and was released in 1990. The typeface is ideal for use in books, newsletters, and packaging because of its classical and elegant aesthetic as well as its functional qualities that make the text type highly readable.

Gotham is designed by Tobias Frere-Jones and was inspired by a mid-20th century signage in New York. It is one of the most used typefaces in the early 21st century.